Growing Roses
The Beginner's Handbook

Nancy N. Wilson

Publisher's Page

Growing Roses
The Beginner's Handbook

By Nancy N. Wilson

ISBN: 978-1-7330941-2-2
© Blurtigo Holdings, LLC

Originally published as:
Growing Roses
Everything You Need to Know and More . . .
Under Pseudonym – Susan Sumner

Updated and Republished under this new title
March 2020 – United States of America

Disclaimer and Terms of Use:

The Author and Publisher have strived to be as accurate and complete as possible in the creation of this book. While all attempts have been made to verify information provided in this publication, the Author and Publisher assume no responsibility for errors, omissions, or contrary interpretation of the subject matter herein. Any perceived slights of specific persons, peoples, or organizations are unintentional. In practical advice books, like anything else in life, there are no guarantees of outcomes resulting from information in this book.

DEDICATION

To my beautiful granddaughter, Bella

**Like the rose, you are a beauty in every way!
Thank you for being one of the great joys of my life**

...for buying my book!

If you like it, please be kind and review on Amazon.com.

Nancy N. Wilson

Please Visit my Websites

https://nancynwilson.com
https://mamaslegacycookbooks.com

Table of Contents

Preface

Whether you are enjoying the rich fragrance and glorious colors of three long-stem rosebuds freshly cut from your garden as you quietly sip your first cup of coffee, or are joyfully accepting the surprise gift of a single rose from someone you love, a rose is always met with a smile and a sweet softness in the heart. It symbolizes everything beautiful in life.

The rose is the most beloved flower of all time! It is intricately intertwined with the mystique of love and romance. It captures the essence and allure of love – young love, mature love, and perhaps even the love of life! There is a universal response to roses by people of all ages that no other flower engenders. Is it any wonder that it is so popular?

Flowers are a great addition to any garden, and/or room's decor. They add color, fragrance, and elegance in spaces that may otherwise be drab and boring. Nothing can offer quite as much instant beauty as a great floral arrangement, especially if those flowers are roses.

For centuries, roses have come to characterize great taste and eternity during events such as weddings, anniversaries, and birthdays. They are always the flower of choice when someone is hoping to create a bond with another.

Anyone can purchase roses in a gift shop or florist, but it takes a special person to want to grow roses. There is a belief by some that these incredible flowers are difficult to handle . . . and I am not talking about the thorns. They have the reputation of being difficult taskmasters.

There may be a bit of truth to those rumors if your goal is to become a national champion with your award-winning roses, which BTW will require above and beyond care. But, for you, me, and everyone who simply wants to enjoy them in our garden for personal delight, the rumors are untrue. Growing roses may require a little more care than other flowers, but not much. They are not the "mighty monsters" that many people claim.

If you are new to the world of growing roses, this book provides a nice introduction with an overview of roses and their varieties, as well as step-by-step tips to help you care for your new amazing plants.

By the time you have finished reading this, you will be prepared to add the beauty of roses to your garden.

How to Use the Book

My goal for the book is to help you as much as possible with this delightful new adventure. There is a lot to absorb in one reading, so relax and enjoy it. Note the sections that you will want to read again for better understanding.

At first glance, you may feel a bit overwhelmed by all of the things that you need to know before you can begin to plant your roses, but that will soon disappear after you read all of the easy to follow instructions outlined in this guide.

The information will help you choose the types of roses that suit your preferences and personality; it will help you understand the climate in your area and choose roses that will do well under those conditions.

It will also give you direction on the when and how to plant your roses to make sure they survive whatever Mother Nature throws at them - the freezing cold or the blazing summer heat. Mother Nature can be a challenge, but you can protect the roses from her wrath most of the time.

At the end of the book, there is a glossary to help you "learn the language" of rosarians. It is great fun to "talk the talk" with others, who love, grow and care their roses – one of the most beloved flower families in the world.

Types of Roses

Let's begin at the beginning by introducing you to the types of roses. As you read through the following information, don't be stressed by all the different types, your choices will be easier than you think. Simply choose the ones that appeal to you, keeping in mind the primary reason you have decided to plant roses.

One of the most common ways that the roses are grouped is through the date of introduction.

Roses	Description
Species Roses	These have been growing in the wild for hundreds, if not thousands, of years
Old Garden Roses	Introduced before 1867, which was the year the hybrid tea rose 'La France' was introduced
Modern Roses	Roses introduced in 1867 or later

Roses are divided by sub-categories within their larger classifications, usually identified by their physical characteristics, such as their growing habits, foliage traits, or even their flower forms.

The modern rose category includes those that are readily available, so let's take a look at the characteristics of each type.

Modern Roses	Description
Hybrid Tea	Upright plant; tall, high centered; blooms continually throughout the season; long-stemmed; generally one bloom per stem; classic rose used for cut flowers; not usually good for the novice grower
Floribunda	Compact bush hardier than hybrid teas; blooms continually throughout the season; fragrant, smaller blooms than hybrid teas; grow in clusters on short stems; good for cutting; a beautiful combination of hybrid tea and polyanthus
Grandiflora	Upright plants; high centered; single or in clusters on tall plants; stems long enough for cutting; lots of colorful blooms
Polyantha	Compact, hardy, can grow quite large (height and width); generous small blooms in large clusters
Shrub	Large plants; hardy and easy to grow; great for landscaping; many color choices; bloom continually throughout the season; disease resistant; require less maintenance.
Miniatures	Smaller versions of larger modern roses; bush sizes range from 6 inches to 6 feet (most commonly 1 to 2 feet); leaves and flowers in perfect proportion; great color for small spaces; good for cold climates; also good indoors in pots
Climbers	Mixed group; long, arching canes in need of support; can be trained to grow vertically or horizontally like vines on trellises, arches, or walls; some bloom only in the spring, others throughout season; group includes climbing hybrid tea, climbing floribunda, climbing Grandiflora, hybrid Wichurana, large-flowered climber, climbing miniature classes
Knockout Roses	The latest entry into the rose family; easy to grow shrub 3' X 3', clusters of 3-inch flowers; light and delicate fragrance; bloom throughout the season; not good for cutting

Choosing the Right Roses

You may be tempted to just run to the nearest nursery or home-gardening center and pick the most beautiful rose plant you see; but, I encourage you to put more thought into it than that. After all, you will be investing both your time and money into this project – and you want it to be successful. A little research would be wise.

To help you make the best choice for your garden, consider the following:

- Why have you decided to plant roses? Do you want season-long color; do you want a sprawling plant that will cover a large area; do you want to fill a small space with color; do you want long-stemmed roses that can be cut frequently for inside enjoyment, etc.? This is an important point that should be clear before you begin your decision-making process.

- Color may seem like a trivial matter, but not if you have a personal preference for specific colors. Since there are so many choices, pick colors that are personally appealing.

- If certain fragrances invoke an allergic reaction for you or any member of your family, you will want to plant roses that have a softer fragrance.

- Rose plants come in all sizes! The final growth height of a rose bush should be considered carefully. What is the size of the space that you want to fill – height and width? Do you want a large climbing plant than can grow up to 30 feet? Or are you looking for a smaller, more delicate version of a climber to grace the small arbor in your garden?

- How much time do you have to invest in the flower? If you have the time and energy to get intimately involved with the plant, hybrid tea roses are a good choice, but they require regular pruning and are prone to disease. Other equally beautiful choices are much hardier and require less maintenance.

- What is the climate of your area? If you have very cold winters, you want a rose that will survive during the offseason. If you have very hot summers, you must choose a rose that will withstand the heat during the blooming season. I recommend that you check the *USDA Plant Hardiness Zone Map,* which will help you make a good decision about the type of rose that will thrive in your climate.

- After you have narrowed your choices down to two or three, go deeper with your investigation. Talk to your nurseryman or research online. Study the pros and cons of choosing one type of rose over another.

- If you are hoping to cut your roses for display inside your home or use them in creating bouquets, you must choose a type that is compatible with this purpose. Hybrid teas are a good choice. Be aware that some roses will fall apart at the petals if they are cut.

- Consider what *other* types of flowers or plants are in your garden, or that you intend to add to your garden. You want to add plants and flowers that will not create a damaging environment for your rose's ecosystem.

Planting Roses

Planting roses does not have to be difficult. With some basic knowledge and key steps for planting, you can plant and nurture a single rosebush or create a magnificent rose garden.

Helpful Tips for Planting your Roses

- Check with your local gardening center for the best type of roses to grow in your climate.

- If you are a novice, you should look for disease-resistant types of roses because they require less maintenance.

- Spring planting is the best.

- Most roses require at least six hours of good sunlight daily (morning sun is best). Adequate sunlight is key to growing beautiful roses. Even those that are considered shade compatible will need a minimum of four hours. Some climbing roses will thrive in partial shade.

- ***DO NOT knock your head against that brick wall by filling a shaded space with a rose plant that needs sun.***

- There must also be good air circulation around your roses. They will not grow well in an enclosed or tight area.

- The soil must be well-drained. Roses do not like soggy soil. Don't plant where water tends to stand idle after a rain. If you don't have a good well-drained area, one solution is to build a raised flower bed.

- Check the PH level of the soil. This is the single most important element in the soil. The ideal amount of acid in the soil is 6 to 6.5 but roses can do well with a range of 5.6 to 7.2. You can get a testing kit for your soil at any garden center. It is much easier to take care of this before you plant than to try to correct after you plant.

- Clear any existing vegetation from the site you have chosen, dig and turn the soil at least two feet deep. For every three buckets of soil add one bucket of organic material (compost or manure) to improve the nutrient content in the soil.

- Dig a proper hole – two feet across and two feet deep for each plant. This provides adequate space for the root system to reach and grow properly. If the hole is too small, fungal infections are more likely.

- Get specific instructions from the nursery on how to prepare the rose bush and the hole for planting. These instructions will vary depending on whether the plant is bare-root or container-grown.

- During the first 3-4 weeks after planting, water the roses often. Deep watering helps the roots push deep into the soil, which will allow them to do better in long-hot dry seasons. Roses need a lot of hydration and food to remain healthy.

- Four weeks after planting, you should start soaking the bed regularly, every week or two - early morning for best results. It would be wise to check with your local nursery for the best watering schedule for your climate conditions.

- Begin fertilization approximately three months after planting. Use organic materials as much as possible. Use 3-6 inches of mulch to control the moisture, temperature, and to stop weeds from coming up. Mulch will also help to lock in the vital nutrients your roses need to remain healthy.

Watering Roses

Watering your roses can be a tricky thing. It is one of the most important aspects of taking care of your roses. Roses need almost as much water to stay healthy as people do. Of course, there are quite a few things that must be considered before you water your roses.

Points to Remember

- Roses love water, but they hate standing in pools of water. Be sure that the area around them drains well.

- On average they require approximately one to two inches of water every week – and even more in hotter, very dry periods. A good rule of thumb is to water your plants two to four times a week for approximately 30 minutes a session.

- Be sure to water in the early morning so that the leaves have time to dry before nightfall. If leaves don't dry before the sun goes down, they may develop a fungal disease.

- Periodically check the depth to which the water is penetrating. Make sure the moisture is reaching the complete root system. You would be surprised how large the root system area is – especially for larger, established roses. The root system could be as deep as a foot or a foot and a half.

- You will learn quickly enough how much water your plant needs. Part of it depends on the type of soil you have – sandy soil needs more frequent watering than heavier clay soils.

- If you are over-watering, the leaves will turn yellow and may eventually drop off. If you are under-watering, the leaves will go limp and sag.

- You may want to shower the plants once a week. This provides the plant with much-needed humidity and cleans dust, dirt, and even spider mites off the leaves. BUT – this *must be done in the early morning* so they are completely dry before nightfall.

- To help you lower the risk of your roses getting diseases, mulch is a nice way to keep the soil moist, without allowing all of the fungal problems caused by too much moisture. Mulch also helps deter the growth of weeds around the plant.

- Good mulch choices are wood chips and stray or dry grass clippings. Apply the mulch two to three inches deep.

- The decomposition of mulch can strip the soil of nutrients so fertilizer will be necessary.

Fertilizing Roses

A good fertilizing program is more than just a bunch of . . . well, you get the idea. Fertilizing is the way you ensure that your roses receive their share of nourishment to keep them looking beautiful for years to come.

If you decide to use a mulch to protect your plant in other ways, you must use fertilizer; but, fertilizing your plant is a good idea whether you use mulch or not.

Be careful using chemical fertilizers, herbicides, and pesticides because they destroy natural soil organisms and disrupt the natural relationship between the roses and the soil. Without helpful bacteria to protect the roots, harmful fungi develop and harm the plant.

The rose plants also become addicted to chemical fertilizers to the point that they will not bloom well without them. The more you use the chemicals, the more the roses depend on them. Organic fertilizers are always the best first choice.

General Guidelines for Fertilizing

- Species roses only need annual spring fertilization.

- All others – fertilize in the spring and add a second application around mid-June or towards the end of the spring blooming period.

- If you have any repeat-bloomers, consider a third application of fertilizer in the middle of July.

- Whatever you do – do not apply any fertilizer after mid-August. You don't want to encourage growth that could be damaged by the upcoming winter months.

- You should never fertilize plants that are heat or water-stressed. Water-stressed plants that grow under a lot of heat will suffer leaf and bud burn.

- Fertilize when there is a steady air temperature of approximately 70-80 degrees so that your plants will absorb the most nutrients possible.

- For best results when you spread fertilizer, use the following optimal approach: Spread the fertilizer out in a circular band around the plant, about half a foot from its crown. Make the width of the applied fertilizer about 18 inches wide. Work the fertilizer in lightly, then water it. This ensures that the fertilizer gets down to the root system.

- If time is a problem and you cannot keep up with the feeding schedule, there is a good time-release fertilizer called osmocote fertilizer. It is composed of dry, encapsulated nutrients that are released slowly throughout the growing season. They are released in four-, six-, or even eight-month intervals, depending on the formula. Osmocote should be applied in May (one-half cup per plant).

Pruning Roses

With few exceptions, pruning is critical for most roses. Climbers are the exception – they should be pruned, but not as frequently as other types of roses.

Pruning requires time and effort. Some rose gardeners do it begrudgingly; but for me, the benefit is worth the hard work.

It is important to learn to prune your roses correctly so they can grow to the peak of perfection. It takes diligence and a steady hand, but it is worth it.

The purpose of pruning is to remove dead and damaged pieces. It also allows new growth to move in an outward direction.

Finally, when a rose bush is pruned properly, the air circulates correctly, which is necessary for the plant to stay healthy.

Pruning Techniques – to Guide You Through the Process

- Early spring is the time to prune. If you live in a temperate climate, prune when the temperatures begin to rise.

  Find out what is the proper time to prune in Region 6 in the USA

- In cold climates, get out your pruning shears when the snow begins to melt. If in doubt, check with a local nursery regarding the ideal time for your climate.

- **Pruning is necessary to protect your roses from disease and insects.**

- To prune the smaller branches, buy a good pair of *hand shears*. Thicker branches that are the size of a pencil (or larger) should be pruned with *loppers*. Always wear a pair of heavy thorn-proof, rose-pruning gloves.

- *Anvil shears* crush the stems, which makes the plant more susceptible to disease. *Bypass pruning shears* that work like scissors are a better choice. They do not damage the plant in the pruning process.

- Sharpen your hand shears each year to ensure the best possible outcome.

- Even though climbers are pruned every other year, you have to be more careful when pruning them. Their branches grow differently than other roses. They crisscross and overlap, which makes it easy to cut off the wrong branches.

- Protect your roses from diseases and insects that result from pruning by soaking your shears in a 1:1 solution of water and bleach.

- Begin the pruning process by removing the wood that is black inside and out (the deadwood).

- Then, remove all small stems that are thinner than a pencil. When you have finished pruning, the bush should have approximately five, dark green, healthy branches that are roughly the size of a pencil.

- Remove all overlapping branches. These are the ones that are susceptible to disease. *What is a overlapping*

- Each bush should look like a vase, with an open center. Do a final check to ensure there are no crossed or touching branches.

- To promote outward growth, cuts should be inward sloping at a 45° angle with the bud facing out.

- The experts recommend pruning your bushes by a third to a half. You can choose the height you prefer. Healthy canes should be one to four feet long.

- Make your cuts above the buds on the outside of the bush, which lets the buds grow upward. They can then open upward with good air circulation, which produces beautifully shaped roses.

Caring for Roses

Roses have the reputation of being difficult to care for, but in reality, that is not completely true.

If you have chosen your roses carefully, selected a type that accommodates your climate, and have been careful in the planting process, you should have minimal problems.

Many small things have to be done to keep your roses looking their best. To make it easier, create a simple schedule of the things that need to be done and when to do them. Then, follow your schedule and soon it will all be part of your normal routine.

Great Tips for the Regular Upkeep of Your Roses

- Be sure you cover the "trinity of care" – fertilizing, watering, and grooming. Roses love to eat and must have the proper nutrients; they need a good water supply on a regular schedule, and they have to be groomed. (See detailed instructions for each in previous sections.)

- Smart rose gardeners mulch. It lessens the required maintenance. Mulching prevents disease, minimizes weeds (and weed removal), and results in less watering. Use organic mulches – grass clippings, wood chips, and pine needles are all good choices.

- Roses need good air circulation. Your garden should be clear and open. Never plant roses in a tight area where the air cannot move.

- The biggest dangers to roses are pests and disease. Do your homework and do what is necessary to protect your plants from harm.

- It is critical to prepare your roses for cold weather. Two options are available for protecting most roses from winter temperatures.

  1) Before the cold weather sets in (preferably late fall), mix a protective covering of manure and compost and completely cover the base of each plant.

  2) Don't prune in the fall. The deadwood will protect the core of the plant by catching the frost. Both methods work. Experiment with each to find the one that works best in your area and for your plants.

- We *do not* recommend using white plastic cones. They have no place in a beautiful rose garden and they trap too much heat when winter begins to thaw.

Preventing Common Rose Diseases

Roses are susceptible to diseases; some types are more susceptible than others. Many of the problems that come with having roses are relatively easy to take care of, but it is always better to prevent them rather than having to cure them later.

Steps to Prevent Diseases from Reaching Your Roses

- If you want to avoid disease problems as much as possible, buy roses that are more disease resistant and low maintenance like shrubs and landscape roses.

- Planting your roses properly in areas that have a lot of sunlight l(at least six hours in the morning), with adequate air circulation and good compost for faster draining can prevent many problems later.

- Keeping different types of flowers and plants in with your roses will help to provide your roses with a better and more balanced ecosystem surrounding it.

- It is important to properly fertilize your plants. Roses need their food too! (see the section on *fertilizing* roses for the best methods)

- Watering your roses in early morning hours will help to keep fungal diseases from hitting your roses. (see the section on *watering* roses for the best techniques)

- A two-inch layer of mulch at the base of your roses will help keep soil-borne diseases at bay.

- Watch for any indication of disease or pest problems and take care of the issues immediately. Wishing it weren't so will not make the problems go away.

Handling Disease and Pest Problems

No matter how hard you try and even with the best prevention techniques in place, you will not always be able to stop disease and pest infestation from affecting your roses. Don't worry, there are solutions! All it takes is a little bit of tender loving care, and the right techniques.

Tips to Help Solve Pest Infestation and Disease Problems

- Act early and act often. Catch the problem in the early stages and it will be easy to resolve.

- The best line of defense is always a natural approach. If you don't have to resort to chemicals, don't!

- Roses attract aphids and beetles. Aphids are the biggest problem you will face.

- First step: If you see aphids, knock them off with squirts of water. Be sure to rinse off the underside of the rose foliage to remove any mites hidden from view. Clean foliage is healthy foliage.

- If that doesn't work, several good pesticides are available that can take care of aphids very quickly.

- If you prefer organic solutions, look for insecticidal soaps that can be found at your local nursery or a home improvement store.

- Beetles – The most common is the Japanese beetle. They will quickly destroy a bloom. If you see a beetle, it is too late to save the bloom. Some experts advise using Malathion, Diazinon, or other insecticides as soon as you see the beetle and continue to apply the formula regularly.

- The organic solution for beetles is to plant garlic plants near your roses and the beetles will stay away. You can also find a garlic spray that will have the same effect.

- Roses are particularly susceptible to three types of diseases: Black Spot, Powdery and Downy Mildews, and Rose Rust. Each of these is a fungus infection and each can be treated with a fungicide. At the very first sign of disease, apply the fungicide. ***Don't procrastinate!*** As part of the treatment – always remove all dead and seriously infested leaves and stems.

- You may even want to take preventative measures by applying the fungicide if you know that hot and humid weather is approaching.

- A good home remedy for powder mildew is to make a mixture of 1 gallon of water, 2 tablespoons of baking soda, 1 tablespoon of *Murphy's Oil Soap* and spray over the roses in the morning every two weeks until the overall temperature around the roses reaches 80° F.

- Midge are tiny maggots that cause the rose's buds to blacken from the damage. If you want to fix this problem, prune the affected area and then destroy it.

Growing Roses Organically

Organic is the magic word in today's world. Organic farming and gardening have become a way of life.

Organic gardening meant growing things naturally, without pesticides and fertilizers filled with chemicals. It is a choice farmers and gardeners make to respect and support the entire eco-system.

There is a huge demand for all things organic, which has changed the way farmers care for their crops and produce meat. So, it is not surprising that flower gardeners also want to grow their plants organically, as well.

Roses are prone to disease and pest infestations, which can be challenging. Steps must be taken to protect the plants; but, most people don't like to use insecticides and pesticides to keep their roses healthy.

Fortunately, there are organic options.

Step-by-step Method for Growing Roses Organically

1. Plant each bush with a foot of space around it to ensure good air circulation. This helps prevent leaf disease.

2. Plant organic roses (bare-root plants are best). Look for blemish-free plants with sturdy green stems and evenly-spaced leaves close together.

3. Prepare the soil for good drainage. Raised flower beds can be a good choice if drainage is a problem.

4. Talk to a knowledgeable local nursery employee about how to prepare organically correct soil.

5. Before you plant bare-root roses, soak them in compost tea in a large container for several hours.

6. When planting bare-root roses, the soil line should be level with the point where the stem and the root meet. If you live in an area with extremely cold winters, plant the stem/root meeting point one to two inches below the soil line.

7. As you prepare to plant the bare root roses, check the roots. If they are in a tight circle, use a very sharp knife to slice straight down each of the four sides. Plant in a hole that is at least two times as wide and two inches deeper than the container.

8. Prepare the garden soil by mixing equal portions of compost and organic garden soil. Gently spread the roots into the soil mix with your hands.

9. Be sure to mulch. It prevents exposure to weeds and complications from water stress. It also reduces maintenance requirements.

10. Use organic fertilizer and water on a regular schedule.

11. When you plant your roses, water them deeply. Then, water in the early morning, once a week during the growing season to promote deep root growth. The number of times you water each week should be determined by your climate.

12. Once a month, cultivate the top one inch of soil around each rose bush; and work a good balanced organic, granular type of fertilizer into the soil. A second option is to use a seaweed-based product or fish emulsion that can be mixed with water. Either one has the nutrients needed to create healthy plants. Carefully read labels to verify ingredients include calcium, nitrogen, potassium, iron, and phosphorus.

13. Insects and pests can be a major problem. You must protect your plants from them. Place sticky yellow bars every 10 feet to catch them.

14. If you have a serious problem, there are organic pesticides you can use.

15. In the worst-case scenario, consider using insecticidal soap as a spray to get the situation under control.

You now have the basic necessary information to grow earth-friendly roses.

There is no need for concern. Your roses will be equally beautiful to those grown through ordinary methods – and they will probably be healthier and live longer, as well.

Organically grown roses tend to have beautiful color, strong immune systems, and outstanding fragrances.

Boosting Your Roses in the Spring

Every spring people get a boost of energy. It is like the very air in the springtime is rejuvenating in itself. Natural passions and new loves are often born in the spring, and old loves get a nice spark between them.

The same goes for roses. It is in the spring that people beginning planting or replenishing their rose gardens. Buds will begin to appear on established bushes.

You may want to try this special tonic that is used to give your roses a strong boost of nutrients they need for them to remain strong and healthy and to produce many blooms throughout the season.

Mix the following ingredients in a 5-gallon tub or bucket:

> 2 cups of alfalfa meal
> 2 cups of Epsom salt
> 2 cups of fish meal
> 2 cups of gypsum
> 2 cups of greensand
> 1 cup of bone meal

- Apply in the early spring after you have removed any necessary winter protection that you may have had in place.

- Pull back the mulch that has been placed around the plants.

- Work one cup of the tonic into the top one inch of soil for smaller bushes.

- Use a trowel or a hand cultivator for larger bushes (bushes six feet or taller). The taller bushes will need three or four cups.

- Replace the mulch and water your roses very well.

Extra Tip #1: You can do this again in the middle of June if you want to keep your roses blooming. Just gently scratch two cups of the mixture into the soil.

Extra Tip #2: You should wear a dust mask while you are mixing the tonic.

Drying Roses

People dry roses for many reasons – as a memento of a significant life moment – or a gift from a friend, a loved one, or a lover.

Regardless of the reason, it is important to dry them properly.

There are two inexpensive and relatively easy ways to dry roses.

Air Drying – The Easiest and Least Expensive

- The most important factor is that the rose (or roses) are in perfect condition. If they are not, there is a good chance they will wither and lose their petals.

- Be sure the branches are completely clean – no residual leaves.

- Put them in a bunch that fans out.

- Use a string or rubber band to tie them together at the bottom.

- Find a dark, dry place to hang them upside down for two to three weeks. This should be enough time for them to dry completely.

Sand Drying

- Pick roses from your garden that are in perfect condition. They must be dry from the top of the petals to the bottom of the stem. Remove any dampness by carefully patting down each rose with a clean paper towel.

- Use florist wire or white glue to reinforce the stems and the blossom.

Florist Wire Reinforcement

- o Cut the stem to about one inch.

- o Cut a three-inch piece of florist wire and push it through the stem – up through the flower.

- o Make a hook with the top of the wire over the head of each rose. Pull it down carefully and attach it securely to the stem.

White Glue Reinforcement

- o Dilute the glue with a few drops of water in a disposable cup.

- o Using a toothpick, place a thin coat of the diluted glue at the base of each petal. After the glue hardens it will keep the petal from falling off.

- Place a thin cost of glue from the base of the rose petals to the end of the stem. After the glue is completely dry, continue as instructed below.

- Put several inches of sand in the bottom of a deep open box – deep enough for the roses to "stand."

- Stand the roses in the sand and slowly pour the sand carefully and evenly around the sides – over and under the petals. (Care must be taken so you don't damage their shape).

- Completely cover the roses and make sure that the roses remain "standing."

- Store the box in a warm, dry place with plenty of light for two to three weeks. The light helps maintain their bright color.

- Drying in humid weather mutes the color.

- At the end of the storage time, carefully pour out the sand by tipping the box over slightly so the sand can fall off the roses.

- Gently remove the roses from the sand one at a time.

Beautiful dried flowers have many uses – as colorful room décor in your home, to brighten up your office, or to give as gifts to friends, colleagues, and loved ones.

Selecting Cold Climate Roses

Most roses will grow just about anywhere and in any type of climate. However, there are a few that simply do not function well in cold climates, for example, Hybrid Tea Roses do not do well with cold weather. They must be grown in a warmer climate like Florida. They simply don't have the necessary winter protection that is required to survive the winter weather.

If you live in an area that is prone to harsh winters, check with your local garden center to find out which rose plants will thrive in your area. Otherwise, you will be wasting your time and money by planting roses that cannot survive in cold climates.

Although the choices are somewhat limited, cold climate roses are wonderful for several reasons. They are very low maintenance flowers, which is especially good for the novice. Cold climate roses are very hardy and have built-in protection against diseases and bacteria that can plague other types of roses.

Below is a shortlist of the ones I would recommend. Of course, there are more, but this is a good start.

Cold Climate Roses

Rugosas
Griffith Buck
Modern Roses
Centrifolias
Species Roses
Gallica
Alba
Shrub Roses

No matter where you live, you can enjoy the beauty of roses in your garden.

~ BONUS ~
Reviving Wilted Cut Roses

Roses add elegance that is unsurpassed by any other flower wherever they are placed.

As beautiful as roses are, they do have a certain vulnerability that is common to any cut flower. They are prone to sag, droop, and wilt after a few days in a vase. Everyone would like to preserve that beauty for as long as possible, and I have a secret that will help save your roses when this happens to you.

- Remove the roses from the vase.

- Separate the roses, but keep them submerged in lukewarm water as you do it.

- Make a fresh cut on the stem, again while it remains in the water because you don't want to expose the stem to air.

- Take each flower, one by one and roll them in newspaper and close the paper with a rubber band to keep it from unrolling.

- Put each rose while still wrapped in the newspaper in a sink or tub filled with water and let them soak for several hours while still separate.

- Once they have soaked, unwrap them carefully, and place them in a vase of fresh warm water.

- If you want to preserve the health of your roses, put some 7UP® in the water to help prevent any bacteria that can clog up the stem.

Extra tip: Roses droop for one of two reasons. Either they were cut too early, or they were out of water too long before putting them into the vase.

Conclusion

If this book has furthered your knowledge about growing roses, fueled your love for them, and helped to establish even one plant in your garden, it has been well worth the time and energy I put into writing it.

This may be the first book you have bought on growing roses, but I am hoping it won't be your last.

Enjoy your new adventure and the thrill of seeing that first amazing bud begin to open. Watch them grow in your garden, enjoy the sweet fragrances, and bask in their beauty as you grace your home with a single rose or a full bouquet.

Enjoy the experience!

Nancy N. Wilson

References

The American Rose Society. www.ars.org

Belendez, K. *Grandma's mason jar*. Retrieved 15 Jun 09 from
    http://scvrs.homestead.com/Cuttings1.html.

Better Homes and Gardens. *Protect roses from pests &
    diseases*. Retrieved 14 Jun 09 from
    http://www.bhg.com/gardening/flowers/roses/prot
    ect-roses-from-pests-diseases/, accessed 14 Jun 09

Climate Zones for Roses, What Are They? Retrieved 14 Jun 09
    from
    http://www.ars.org/About_Roses/climate_zones-
    whatarethey.html.

GardenStewBlog. *How to transplant roses and prune roses*.
    Retrieved 14 Jun 09 from
    http://www.gardenstew.com/blog/e283-86-how-to-
    transplant-and-prune-roses-graphic-heavy.html.

Garden-Web. http://forums.gardenweb.com/forums

HelpMeFind. Retrieved 15 Jun 09 from
    www.helpmefind.com/roses

Iannotti, M. *Growing miniature roses*. Retrieved 17 Jun 09
    from
    http://gardening.about.com/od/rose1/a/MiniRose.ht
    m

Ondra, N. J. (2001). *Taylor's Guide to Roses.* Houghton-Mifflin Publishing, NYC, NY.

Owen, D. *Raising Roses and Your Climate Zone.* Retrieved 14 Jun 09 from http://ezinearticles.com/?Raising-Roses-and-Your-Climate-Zone&id=493622.

Patton, D. *Watering roses.* Retrieved 15 Jun 09 from http://extension.missouri.edu/extensioninfonet/article.asp?id=1504.

Watering Roses. *Roses love water.* Retrieved 7 April 2012 from http://www.rose.org/watering-roses/.

Appendix I
Glossary of Terms

Below is a quick-reference glossary of many (but by no means all) of the terms you may encounter as you continue on with your love affair with roses.

Term	Definition
Anther	The upper portion of the stamen; contains the pollen sacs
Apical Meristem	Cells which did not mature at the tip of shoots and roots producing the hormone auxin
Auricle	The "earlike" project on the tip of the stipule
Auxin	The hormone regulating the bloom cycle
Axil	Angle on upper side where the leaf joins the stem
Axillary	Any bud or branch in the axil of a leaf; these grow following pruning
Bark	Outer layer of the cane of a rose
Bract	A leaf that is usually smaller or shaped differently than others on the plant; grows under the peduncle just below the flower
Bud	Embryonic shoot that will produce either flowers or foliage
Bud union	Area between the roots and stems where the bud of a different plant has been grafted onto the rootstock
Calyx	A series of flower parts which grow from the peduncle; made of sepals, usually green and leaf-like that protect the flower bud
Cane	Stem of the rose -- either the main stem (sometimes called the trunk) or lateral stems and branches

Carpel	An organ which holds the ovules along its margins; part of the compound pistil
Compound leaf	Leaf made of two or more parts or leaflets
Corolla	Second series of flower parts growing from the peduncle; composed of petal
Double	Refers to the number of petals on a bloom, normally agreed to being between 25 and 45.
Filament	Stalk of the stamen supporting the anther
Floral tube	Cup-like structure formed by fusion of the basal parts of the sepals, petals, and stamens.
Fruit	Ripe ovary containing seeds and any adjacent parts
Hip	Fruit of the rose containing the seeds
Leaf	Organ that arises laterally from a shoot apex. Usually flat; may be simple or compound
Leaf scar	Mark left on the stem when the leaf detaches; above each of these is a bud
Meristem	Tissue made of cells that do not mature, but remain capable of growing and dividing; present in growing tips
Mixed buds	Buds that produce both leaves and flowers; usual type of bud on rose; present in leaf axils
Ovary	Swollen basal portion of the pistil containing the ovules or the seeds
Ovule	Structure containing the embryo sac, nucellus, integuments and stalk. Following fertilization this develops into seeds
Peduncle	Main cane of a spray or an individual flower
Pedicel	Stem of an individual flower in a spray
Perianth	Collective term for the calyx and corolla (sepals and petals) combined

Petal	One of the units of the corolla of a flower. Roses have from four to more than 100 petals, depending on the variety
Petiole	Stalk of the leaf
Petiolul	Subdivision of petiole connecting the lateral leaflets to the petiole
Pistil	Central organ of the flower made of one or more carpels; enclosing the ovule
Pith	Soft inner portion of stem
Pollen	Granules within pollen sacs which contain genetic information used for sexual reproduction
Prickle	Spine-like superficial outgrowth of the stem; roses technically have prickles, not thorns
Roots	Underground portions of the rose used for support, and absorption and delivery of water and nutrients
Rootstock	Cultivated roots implanted with a bud of another variety; sometimes called grafting
Semi-double	Refers to number of petals on bloom -- usually 12 to 25 in this category
Sepal	One unit of calyx; green coverings of a flower bud which open to reveal petals; roses normally have five sepals
Single	Refers to number of petals the bloom has -- customarily four to eight
Spray	Several flowers' buds arising from one peduncle; develop into many flowers on short pedicels
Stamen	Organ of flower producing pollen, made of anther and filament
Stigma	Top of pistil, the section that receives the pollen grains

Stipule	Leaf appendage usually present in roses on the petiole where it meets the stem
Style	Portion of the pistil connecting ovary and stigma
Terminal	Buds at the end of branches
Thorn	Branch of a plant that becomes woody, hard, and pointed; not to be confused with prickles
Trunk	Main stem; the cane that eventually produces all the side branches or lateral canes

Growing Roses ©2020

About the Author

Nancy N. Wilson

Nancy N Wilson is a writer, blogger and bestselling author of more than 30 books. She was born and reared in a small farming community in Southern Arizona. She earned a B.S. Degree in Education and Psychology at Utah State University and an MBA at Thunderbird School of Global Management.

She has lived and worked on both the East Coast and West Coast of the United States, consulted with major corporations in Europe and Japan, and traveled extensively throughout Central and South America.

In 2007, she returned to Arizona to live near her two sons and to do what she always wanted to do – WRITE.

She now spends her time contributing to her "Healthy Living Blog, (https://Mamaslegacycookbooks.com), testing new recipes, and writing and publishing non-fiction books – half of which are cookbooks – plus other non-fiction topics that she finds interesting, like rose gardening!

She finds great satisfaction and joy in sharing all she has learned with you, her readers, and hopes that you will benefit and develop a passion for growing roses as great or greater than hers.

There is a complete list of her books on the following page, which can be purchased through Amazon.com as eBooks or paperbacks.

Other Books by This Author

Cookbooks
Candy Making Made Easy - Instructions and 17 Starter Recipes
Cake Making Made Easy - Instructions and 60 Cakes
Cook Ahead – Freezer to Table
SPECIAL DIETS Fresh and Easy Cookbook
Garden Fresh Soups and Stews
Juicing for Life – The Secret to Vibrant Health
Sweet Treats – Candy, Cookies, Cake, Ice Cream, Pudding, and Pie
Tweens and Teens – A Cookbook to Get You Started
Single, On-Your-Own, and Hungry
COOKIES! The Best Collections of Cookie Recipes EVER! Just for YOU!

Mama's Legacy Cookbook Series
Seven Volumes Available
Dinner – 55 Easy Recipes (Volume I)
Breakfast and Brunch – 60 Delicious Recipes (Volume II)
Dessert – 50 Scrumptious Recipes (Volume III)
Chicken – 25 Classic Dinners (Volume IV)
Mexican Favorites – 21 Traditional Recipes (Volume V)
Side Dishes – 60 Great Recipes (Volume VI)
Sauce Recipes – 50 Tasty Choices (Volume VII)

Health and Fitness
DETOX – The Master Cleanse Diet
Growing Tomatoes – Everything You Need to Know, and More
Stop Eating Yourself into an Early Grave
WOW! You Look Fantastic!

Business
Attitude Adjustment
Starting an Online Business
Congratulations, You Are Self-Employed

Books Written under Pseudonyms
Power Up Your Brain – Five Simple Strategies (J. J. Jackson)
Clicker Training for Dogs (Amy Ellsworth)
Making Money with Storage Unit Auctions (Bryce Cranston)

Made in the USA
Monee, IL
29 September 2022

When Life Doesn't Stick
to the Game Plan
...because the doctor has bad news

Carol A. Hacker

Note to the Reader

I wrote this book to inform and educate as well as to share my personal perspective on dealing with serious illness. This book is not designed to advise or instruct you as to specifically what must be done in a particular case. Information contained in this book should not be used to alter a medically prescribed regimen or as a form of self-treatment. It is important to consult with a doctor before undertaking an exercise program, changing your diet, or taking any medications.

The identities of the people in the case histories in this book have been altered to protect the individuals' privacy.

ISBN 0-9662011-3-2

Printed in the United States of America

Cover design by Jonathan Pennell

Books are also available at quantity discount prices. Please contact Carol Hacker at 770-410-0517 in Alpharetta, GA.

Content

PART ONE

PART TWO

PART THREE

Foreward

My medical nightmare began on December 12, 1996. I phoned the neurotologist in Atlanta, Georgia, to get the results of my MRI test. The receptionist answered and immediately put me on hold. My stomach churned; I was stricken with fear. Within thirty seconds the doctor said, "Hello. You have a brain tumor. Chances are it's benign. You need to do something soon." Click. Whew!

I panicked; I immediately fell apart. The words benign and malignant both meant the same to me at that point. Although in reality, the difference between the two is VERY different. However, thoughts of something growing inside of my head petrified me! What would it take to completely remove it? Where would I find a doctor that I could trust? How would the outcome impact my work and my life?

To make matters worse, I was scheduled to leave for New York City on a business trip that afternoon. I called my client and she understood why I had to cancel. I couldn't think about anything but the bad news I had just received. It was the beginning of my personal journey to hell and back.

I titled this book "When Life Doesn't Stick to the Game Plan ...because the doctor has bad news" because that is exactly how I felt about what happened to me. Everything about my life was wonderful and then POW! I was knocked off track and the nightmare began.

Looking back, I assumed that I would always have good health, even though I saw myself as a person who took little for granted and celebrated life every chance I got. Don't we all believe that bad things happen to other people, but not to us? Other people get sick and even die, but it's hard to imagine that happening to us. Well, guess what? Illness and death can and will happen to everyone at some point and totally alter life's game plan!

This book is about living through illness. It is my hope that it will help you transition beyond your illness and that it will help you know what to do in dealing with life's stresses when the doctor has bad news. It is meant to be positive and energizing and at the same time help you accept the realities that you are facing.

Dedication

This book is dedicated to Rick A. Friedman, M.D., PhD., and William E. Hitselberger, M.D. With your incredible skill and loving hearts, you saved my life. "Thank you" will never be enough. And to Robert E. Levine, M.D. You reached out to me as a surgeon as well as a friend. Thank you for all of your support. Bob, you are one in a million! All three of you are part of an incredible team associated with the House Ear Clinic, Inc. in Los Angeles. My research paid off because the time that I invested led me to each of you. You are exceptional in your talents and genuine concern for your patients.

This book is also dedicated to the memory of Dr. Jeffery Williams, the former Associate Professor of Neurosurgery and Radiation Oncology, and Director of Stereotactic Radiosurgery at Johns Hopkins Hospital. Jeff, you gave so freely of your time to everyone in need of your extraordinary expertise. You are loved and missed by all who knew you.

Stephen Preas, M.D., psychiatrist and personal friend—thank you Steve, for helping me recognize that what I was experiencing prior to surgery was normal and that my strong spirit wouldn't let me down.

And for my dear cousin, Brigitte Gonzales, who had this same beastly tumor, and for all of my other tumor buddies who are too many to list without leaving someone out, but you know who you are.

Preface

This book is divided into fifty-eight chapters. There were so many great ideas that came to mind that I felt needed to be included that I found it difficult to leave anything out. The chapters are short and to the point. Yet, each contains important information that I hope will help you on your journey. I've used the word "journey" twice so far in this book because I believe it best describes what happens to us when we embark on the path of change and loss—loss of the person we once were prior to illness and because of illness.

When the doctor has bad news, it seems that most everything changes. In truth, there are many things that do not change. Focus on everything that has not changed about your life.

Change is also closely associated with grief; grief follows a loss. I knew immediately upon being diagnosed that I would have to let go of something and work my way through the grieving process, a process that varies in length and intensity. Some people move quicker than others do. I saw myself as an average person reacting to adversity. Feeling like I was being pulled kicking and screaming by a strange force through a valley of darkness, I started to grieve the loss that I was anticipating. But I did make it through and have long since moved on with my life, and you will do the same.

Change is part of living for all of us, whether we like it or not. How you choose to handle change as related to your health has a lot to do with acceptance, healing, and looking forward to the future.

And with that thought I begin my writing. I hope that the information in your hands will help you face the medical challenges that led you to this book. No one said that life is easy. It's only when we truly get to know people that we learn of the roadblocks they too have confronted and overcome.

Acknowledgements

I want to extend a special "Thank you" to the following people who generously volunteered their time to proof-read, edit, and provide feedback on this book. They are listed in alphabetical order as they are equally important to me.

Christine Brininstool
Brother Frank Mazsick, CFX
Susan McCreary
Woody McKay
Jeanne Sharbuno

In addition, there are five dear friends who have set the example for all survivors. You are amazing!

Rosemary Ferris
Bruce Kaufman
Dennis McClellan
Rene Newcorn
Donna Thiraveja

Thank you for being the wonderful people that you are. My life has been greatly enriched because of our friendships. The world is a better place because of each of you!

Introduction

Journal Entry
December 12, 1996

At 8:37 this morning I phoned my doctor's office to get the results of my MRI test. The doctor got on the phone and matter-of-factly told me that I have a brain tumor. I hung up and started to cry. All I could think about was, "I can't believe it! There must be a mistake! This can't be happening to me!" I'm spinning around in circles as my two cats watch with frightened looks on their little faces. Just when my life was on a roll, the world came crashing down on me. I will remember this day forever...

How ironic that I lost my beloved father to a heart attack exactly 14 years ago today. I have never stopped missing him and when this shocker knocked me off my feet, I immediately reached out to him, but I couldn't even feel his presence. Where was he when I needed him most? He was such a wonderful, loving, and sensitive man who was always there to kiss my hurts away and assure his little girl that everything would be okay. I desperately need him now. "Daddy where are you? Daddy can you hear me? Daddy can you make this terror go away?"

All I really know about the tumor is that "It is a major surgery to remove it." Those were the exact words of the technician who ran the brain scan tests prior to the MRI.

I assumed that a tumor like mine (an acoustic neuroma) could easily be cut out, since it generally starts growing in the auditory canal. I had already lost most of my hearing by the time the tumor was discovered and resigned myself to total deafness in one ear. But I guess I'm getting ahead of myself. My immediate concern is the business trip, for which I am scheduled to leave for the airport in three hours. Should I call my client? Can I separate myself emotionally and keep this commitment?

No, I just cannot talk myself into it. I called my client and told her the devastating news. She was completely supportive and very concerned. Thank goodness for clients who are also friends!

I need to start working on a plan. Once I get over the shock I know what I have to do; I did it once before when I lost a job that meant the world to me. I grieved much in the same way that I expect to grieve as a result of this news. (It would be several days before I could get it together enough to tackle the Internet and start my research, but the grieving process started immediately).

"Life doesn't have to be perfect to be wonderful."

—Annette Funicello

PART ONE

PART ONE of this book offers my thoughts for getting started—figuring out what to do when the doctor has bad news. It also includes a variety of ideas for strengthening your resolve to overcome the obstacles you are facing with chapters such as: *Recognize That Knowledge is Power, Adopt a Forward-Thinking Attitude, Listen to Your Intuition* and *Take a "Good News" Inventory.* As you know, a diagnosis of illness can be a mentally paralyzing event, but it does not have to ruin your life.

My own experience taught me that until I believed in myself and my ability to adapt, I could not emotionally move forward, and thus get on with the treatment and healing that I so desperately needed. For that reason, Chapter 1 is very important and is entitled *Trust in Your Ability to Adapt.* The rest of the chapters in PART ONE includes ideas that I personally found helpful and believe that you will too.

No part of this book is meant to be a medical dictionary. There are dozens of books available on specific illnesses, as well as the latest in medical dictionaries. Check your local bookstore. This book is meant to be a motivational tool from the first chapter through the very last. I believe that hope, although very important, is not a strategy. I've tried to offer strategies that I have personally found helpful in healing the mind, body and spirit.

And with that, let's begin our journey into *When Life Doesn't Stick to the Game Plan...*

Chapter 1

Trust in Your Ability to Adapt

Our immediate reaction when the doctor delivers bad news is oftentimes to question our ability to adapt to the changes we are about to face. Depression often follows and may soon interfere with our recovery as well as with acceptance of something we cannot control. These feelings are normal. Unfortunately, they can also be debilitating. What can be done to help in adapting? It is undoubtedly the toughest part of the healing process. "How long will it take? Can I adapt alone, or will I need help?" These are just two of the questions that I asked myself when I found out that I was sick.

Consider this:

Trust in yourself. Think about past situations in which you successfully adapted to change or bad news. How did you handle it then? Could you use the same technique(s) to help you now? In my case, I knew that researching my options would help me adjust to the bad news that I was facing. I knew that the more I learned about my illness, the better off I would be. After I got over the shock, I turned to the Internet and found what I was looking for—lots of information on dozens of web sites.

I also worked on mentally convincing myself to look at the bright side—the doctor was 99% certain that my tumor was benign. Some days I was more successful than other days in staying upbeat; however, I never totally gave up on myself. At times it was incredibly difficult to maintain a positive attitude. Even my body language reflected how I felt and I knew it. It was obviously negative and other people saw it too.

Here is another suggestion: Program your mind into believing you *can* do it. Going through the motions of optimistic thinking and positive self-talk can trigger your emotions and help in your ability to accept change. How long will it take? That is anybody's guess. You may adapt quickly, or you may struggle and mentally fight your way through to acceptance. Some people can do it alone, but most seek help from others; there is no shame in that. In fact, I encourage you to reach out for the help you need.

Make a commitment now to do whatever it takes to build trust in your ability to adapt with or without the support of family and friends, and then go out and do it!

Chapter 2

Reach a Point of Acceptance

One of the keys to recovery is being able to accept the reality of your circumstances. Personally, at times I found that accepting what was happening to me to be nearly impossible. I fought the reality with every ounce of energy I had. I refused to give in to the fact that I had no choice but to face the most horrible surgery that I could imagine, with an outcome of a potentially paralyzed face. It was not until I reached a point of acceptance that I could develop my action plan and move forward.

It took a long time, but it finally happened when I realized that I would slowly become incapacitated and eventually die without the operation. I had to ask myself how I felt about dying relatively young when I didn't have to. I always said that I wanted to die young (in spirit) as late in life as possible, but I did not think that I would be faced with this kind of decision so early in my life. In spite of the risks associated with the surgery, I finally conceded that I had nothing to lose and everything to gain by having the tumor removed.

Consider this:

Educate yourself. Learn as much as you can about your illness. Seek professional counseling if you think that you would benefit from help outside of your family and circle of friends. Get involved with a support group. All three of these activities take time, but they are critical to your recovery. I am not suggesting that any of these things are easy to do. However, I am recommending that you start doing whatever it takes to get to the point where you can accept what is happening to you. If you need help, get it. Until you reach the stage of acceptance, it will be very difficult to take the other steps to healing that are discussed in this book.

Chapter 3

Identify Your Supporters

You have recently been diagnosed with a health problem. Maybe it is diabetes, Parkinson's disease, arthritis, cancer, heart disease, multiple sclerosis, leukemia, macular degeneration or something equally as serious and frightening. The first and normal reaction is shock followed by denial. Initially, you may be numb. You cannot think clearly or concentrate. You may even become depressed. All of these symptoms are the psychological effects of your diagnosis of illness. You may also be dealing with the physical aspects of your illness that can range from mild to severe. Combine the physical with the psychological stress and you may feel like you are in a pressure cooker!

Consider this:

Identify all of your supporters. You are going to need the help of your family and friends as well as the best, most open-minded doctors you can find. Concealing illness from those with whom we are the closest is not a good idea. People who care about you can provide helpful emotional support as well as assist with transportation, meals, and other family and work-related responsibilities. If they are *able* to help, chances are good they *will* help.

In addition, it is not unusual to find that some people do not know what to say, so they avoid you. Maybe they think your illness is contagious. I personally experienced a reaction by a friend who appeared terrified that he, through his association with me, would get a brain tumor. Don't worry about people like him. Educate him if you can; if not, forget it.

Concentrate on those people who can help you; do not waste time and energy on those who appear unwilling or unable to assist you for whatever reason. Then, identify the individuals who will form the basis for your support. Tell them what is occurring and ask for help. Be prepared to graciously accept what they are willing to offer without feeling guilty.

Assistance comes in many forms and may include, but is not limited to people who will:

- Drive you to and from doctor/hospital appointments
- Shop for groceries
- Mail a package
- Take your turn driving for the carpool
- Prepare meals
- Clean your house
- Cut your grass
- Do your laundry
- Run errands
- Give you a foot, or neck and shoulder massage
- Wash your car
- Drop you off at the local library
- Help you with a bath or shower
- Attend support group meetings with you

- Provide reading materials—magazines, books, and newspapers
- Keep you company when you are lonely
- Stay in touch by telephone

Your supporters are essential to your physical and emotional well being. Do not delay in determining who they are and in identifying how they may be able to assist you. Asking for help is not a sign of weakness. There is a lot of reciprocity in life. You have either helped others in the past or will be called upon to do so in the future. This is not the time to be shy either. Give yourself permission to embrace your supporters with open arms and let them help you in any way they are willing.

Chapter 4

Be the Captain of Your Health Care Team

Oftentimes, the shock of bad news derails us—prevents us from thinking rationally at a time when we need to think clearly. Upon diagnosis, life changes in an instant, or so it seems. Unexpectedly, your life's game plan is interrupted and you assume that it is for the worst—a very normal reaction. You may feel as if your life is spinning out of control. At some point, you may actually lose control, but hopefully not for long.

I had some dark moments when I felt like there was no hope. The outcome of the surgery and the possibility of being burdened with horrible side effects for the rest of my life weighed heavily on my mind. I had met numerous people for whom their acoustic neuroma surgery did not go well—their faces were disfigured and they had lost most of their self-esteem. But despite fearing the worst, I knew that I had to take charge of my treatment if I had any hope of a good result for my face following surgery. The first few doctors that I met with assured me that my face would be paralyzed for the rest of my life. Refusing to accept their predictions, I walked out the door and never looked back!

Consider this:

If you are physically and emotionally capable, make the decision right now to become the captain of your health care team. This is YOUR LIFE we are talking about and you are in charge. Manage your situation now just as you have in the past when you have been confronted by a major challenge.

If you cannot do it alone, find someone to help you. Ask yourself if you want a little, some, or a lot of input into your treatment plan. Are you willing to let the medical team make all of the decisions? Consider working in partnership with your physician. Do not be forced into doing something that you don't want to do. Keep in mind that doctors are human; they can make mistakes, as can other members of the medical team. That is why it is so important to be involved in your case to the greatest extent possible.

In addition, some doctors are on the leading edge in terms of the latest treatment methods, clinical trials, and most appropriate medications. Others are less in tune. As captain of your health care team, it is up to you and/or your family and friends to find the doctor(s) and hospital (if needed) that will give you the best chance for a speedy and complete recovery. Once you have identified your team of professionals, take charge by being an informed and involved patient from the very start.

Chapter 5

If There is No Anxiety, You're Dead

Are you feeling anxious? Who would not be? You have received the worst news of your life. You may wonder if you really heard what you think you heard. What you are experiencing seems like a dream—no, more like a terrible nightmare. Take comfort in the fact that the anxiety that you are experiencing is not unusual; it is very normal. If you did not feel some anxiety, you would be dead.

Each of us is unique; we handle adversity differently. Some people cry, while others turn inward and are reluctant to talk. Some get nauseous or vomit or even wet their pants. Others cannot sleep. Stress causes some people to binge on food while others may stop eating. The bottom line is that anxiety is no fun, but you can control these feelings if you are willing to work at it.

But what if you feel like you do not have the necessary coping skills, and you are anxious beyond what you feel you can handle or what you think is normal?

Consider this:

Keep in mind that anxiety is not uncommon, but you may need to get professional help if you are having trouble functioning. Seek the help of a psychiatrist (who is a medical doctor) or a psychologist (who has a Ph.D. in psychology) and share your thoughts and concerns. These specialists can help get you back on track.

Locate the best psychiatrist or psychologist in your community. Consider asking people you know, including your physician(s) for a referral. Make an appointment. After your first appointment, if you don't feel comfortable with the doctor, don't hesitate to find another doctor.

You may need medication to remain calm and help you handle your feelings of anxiousness. It may only be needed for a brief period of time. If you need it longer, so what? Take the necessary steps to bring your emotional life under control.

Whatever you do, make a conscious decision to take action and get yourself out of the state of anxiety that you are in so that you can sleep, eat, and get on with your daily activities and healing. You have a lot of influence over what happens to you regarding your mental health and the associated anxiety and stress.

Chapter 6

Find Others Who Feel Your Pain

Serious illness is frightening. At the very least it is an inconvenience. Some people make a conscious decision to tough it out and handle it alone. Others seek help, even from strangers. There is nothing wrong with that either. The final result is that you can benefit from the support of people who are going through or have gone through what you are experiencing.

Start by making a conscious effort to surround yourself with optimistic, loving, caring and supportive people that can enhance your healing. Many of them feel your pain. Chances are good that there are hundreds, or even thousands of individuals, who can identify with you as you read this book because they have experienced the same or similar things that you are going through. Your job is to reach out and find them.

Consider this:

Locate and contact the national support group that is related to your medical condition. They will send you complimentary information—it is often a comprehensive package that can help you better understand your specific illness. In addition, the national support group can put you in touch with the nearest local or regional support group. They often have toll-free phone numbers. Start with the Internet and/or the telephone book. (See the Appendix of this book for a partial list of organizations).

Local groups typically meet as often as once a week. But it is not just the meetings that are valuable. The contacts you make with people who can give you their perspectives as well as some tips for coping with the psychological and physical challenges offer major benefits. Support group members can provide hope and practical information that could save you a lot of valuable time.

A common bond and life-long friendships are often created among those with the same or similar health issues. Sometimes when family and friends simply do not understand as hard as they try, members of your support group know just what to do to help. Keep in mind that there may not be a support group for every illness, but there is most likely a group that is closely related to what you need.

On another note regarding support groups, your family and friends may need help dealing with their pain as they try to help you. There are support groups for them too, and the organizations listed in the Appendix of this book can lead them to the information they need.

Chapter 7

Turn Fear Into Courage

Fear is a normal, human emotion, especially when the doctor tells you something you do not want to hear. Your ultimate goal is to re-direct your fear into courage. I have never thought of myself as a courageous person. In fact, I am probably one of the least courageous people I know when it comes to medical care. I was initially paralyzed with fear, but I also realized that I had to get over those feelings if I was going to help myself. I knew that I was the best person to help *me*. I also knew that I could not do it alone, and that I would need lots of encouragement from friends and strangers alike.

Consider this:

Fear can make us nervous and unable to complete even the simplest of tasks. Fear wastes energy that could be channeled in a positive direction. A lot of what happens is up to you; fear is a mental thing. Get professional help if you need it, and find a way to turn your fear into courage. It is easier said than done, but it is doable if you are willing to make the commitment to yourself to deal with your illness courageously.

If you are a member of a church or religious organization, this is often a very supportive place to seek help in mustering the courage that you need to move forward.

Here are some other suggestions for turning fear into courage. Stay busy. Be as informed as you possibly can. Talk to as many people as you can that have gone through the same experience. Your support group is also a great resource, as you will interact with people who share your pain.

Chapter 8

Recognize That Knowledge is Power

Everyone who knows me knows that I am always saying, "Knowledge is power." I believe that the more you know about your medical condition, the better informed you are when it comes to making critical decisions concerning your treatment. Do not be afraid of what you might learn. You are better off knowing what to expect than to find out the truth later and still not be able to do anything about it.

I know people who would rather not know the details of their health condition. That is their right, but I would not choose this approach for myself. Terry is an example. He has not done any research to understand the medical care and lifestyle changes that could impact his condition. He keeps his doctors' appointments, but when he is given prescriptions, he laughs as he shreds them when he gets back to his office.

Perhaps, deep inside he wants to know more, but he is not willing to do anything to educate himself. He also does not seem to recognize that he can gain power over his illness with the information he gathers and applies. He can also potentially prevent a medical disaster by following his doctors' recommendations.

Consider this:

If you are interested in learning more about your illness, start with the Internet. Look at web sites for the latest health news.

Try MedlinePlus at www.medlineplus.gov. The U.S. National Library of Medicine and the National Institute of Health jointly provide this site. You might also try www.healthfinder.gov. It has links to more than 1,800 health-related organizations. Bookmark www.nlm.hih.gov which is the U.S. National Library of Medicine that provides information on any health-related topic and the most up-to-date research. The National Women's Health Resource Center at www.healthywomen.org offers lots of information on everything from causes of cervical cancer to breast-feeding advice.

If you do not have a computer, head for your public library. Chances are good that they have a computer that is connected to the Internet—your lifeline to a wealth of current data. Talk to medical professionals and ask them questions. Learn what you need to know to make an informed decision concerning your treatment. I spoke with dozens of people who were familiar with my problem including doctors from throughout the country.

Investigate every detail of what you can expect. Some patients do not want to know anything. I find it difficult to understand those feelings because I don't think it is a wise thing to do. I believe that the more you know, the more prepared you will be for the recovery phase of your illness.

A sample of web sites containing health information include the following:

www.eatright.org (American Dietetic Association)

www.nih.gov (National Institute of Health)

www.fda.gov (U.S. Food and Drug Administration)

www.mayohealth.org (Mayo Clinic)

www.who.int (World Health Organization)

www.cancerhopenetwork.org (Cancer Hope Network)

www.friendshealthconnection.org (Friends Health Connection)

www.medscape.com (WebMD)

www.americasdoctor.com (Chats and Q&A with doctors)

www.centerwatch.com (Lists 40,000 plus clinical trials and new drug therapies)

www.ama-assn.org (Provides information for every licensed physician in the U.S. including medical school attended, year graduated, residency training, specialty and specialty certification)

www.mdanderson.org (The University of Texas M.D. Anderson Cancer Center)

www.mskcc.org (Memorial Sloan-Kettering Cancer Center)

www.yoursurgery.com (Descriptions of operations and diagnostic tests for $5 per report)

www.dartmouthatlas.org (Helps you spot any suspiciously large number of elective procedures in your part of the country)

www.guidelines.gov (Offers standard clinical guidelines for various procedures)

www.ahcpr.gov (Consumer tips for patients, plus databases and links to ensure quality care)

www.medicalconsumers.org (Articles examine effectiveness of different treatments and procedures)

Chapter 9

Throw a "Pity Party" If You Must But...

The "but" is about limiting the amount of the time that you allow for the "party." Wallowing in self-pity is not the best use of time and energy, although for some people it is a "comfortable" feeling. Self-pity can also be a part of the grieving process. You need and deserve time to adjust, but eventually you must face the facts.

In a true story, a woman sat in her hospital bed and cried. A voice inside of her head kept asking her, "Why me?" Another taunting voice inside retorted, "Why not you?" She was hospitalized for a very treatable problem. A nurse heard her crying and stopped to check on her. "I'm having a pity party," the patient said, as she looked up with tears running down her face. "That's okay; there's nothing wrong with that. You're entitled," replied the nurse. "But set a time limit. Allow yourself a maximum of thirty minutes—cry, get angry; both will help in your emotional healing."

The patient gave herself more time to continue her "pity party." Within ten minutes she had stopped crying and came to terms with the fact that nothing would change her medical condition but aggressive treatment, time, and a positive attitude. She decided to put her "pity parties" behind her for good and get on with her recovery.

Consider this:

The emotional side of illness can be devastating. Those who get stuck in the "pity party" state of mind often pull themselves down, take their support team with them, and frequently impact the medical team that is trying to help them.

Take time to grieve, but do not allow your emotions to rule your life. You've got work to do—the most important of which is to get better. Attitude, whether good or bad, plays an important role in your recovery. It is your choice. What goes on in your mind is an "inside job." Even the people closest to you cannot get into your head and make you feel psychologically better. You are the best person for that job.

Chapter 10

Don't Blame Yourself

Sometimes we blame ourselves when life doesn't stick to the game plan. It might not make sense, but for whatever reason we do it anyway. Blaming yourself will not change what has happened to you. It probably will not make you feel any better either.

For example, a smoker developed emphysema that caused her to become dependent upon oxygen twenty-four hours a day. She used much of her valuable energy blaming herself for something she did that was irreversible. It was too late to change the past, but she spent the remainder of her life beating herself up over a decision to smoke, one that she had made many years ago.

Consider this:

We all make decisions about how we live our lives. Yet, some of us still get heart disease, others contract cancer, and still others have to face even bigger challenges. Many of our health problems are out of our control. We have done everything right, but we still get sick. Some of us have an inherited or genetic disease. The energy that it takes to blame ourselves for something that we possibly could have prevented is energy lost. Punishing ourselves for something over which we have no control is equally foolish.

Consider making a pledge to yourself right now to stop blaming YOU. Blame is a negative activity; it rarely leads to anything productive. Each time you slip into the mode of blaming yourself, try forcing yourself to think about something else. Practice pushing guilt and blame out of your conscious mind so that you can get on with living.

The following tips can help you to forget about blame and focus on fun and more productive things:

- Call a friend and talk about the good old days
- Eat something you have never eaten before
- Get some fresh air, especially if you work inside
- Do some volunteer work
- Take a different way home from work
- Sign up for an improv class
- Take the dog for a walk
- Throw a party
- Break an unspoken rule that won't hurt anyone
- Take an art history class
- Get a temporary tattoo
- Take dancing lessons
- Learn how to play a musical instrument
- Go for a walk in the rain
- Drink a glass of soy milk
- Make an effort to smile more
- Mentor a friend
- Dunk your cookies in your milk
- Do something you've been putting off
- Donate a pair of old eyeglasses to the Lion's Club

Chapter 11

Set Your Own Limits

Other people's expectations of you can sometimes be difficult to handle. Only you know how you feel at any given time. Sometimes people unknowingly push you to the point of breaking, thinking they are helping, when in reality they are doing just the opposite. You may have days when you feel pressured by family members or friends to exercise, go shopping, or join in a card game.

I knew exactly what my limits were; I was often exhausted and didn't feel like doing anything but watching television while lying on the couch. However, my concerned family and friends felt that I needed to be doing something much of the time. I finally realized that I was in charge of setting my own limits and did just that. I learned how to say, "no" and feel okay about it.

My tumor buddy, Gerry, had the same type of surgery that I had. I met him for the first time in California at the House Ear Clinic, Inc. while I was recovering in the room next to him. He was a wonderful friend to all of the patients even though he was a patient himself. He even had the energy to minister to the rest of us when we could barely pick our heads up off the pillow.

Gerry shared with me how anxious he felt about the expectations that his family had of him. They had no idea how serious the surgery was and they anticipated that he would be up walking and visiting with them the day after surgery. He needed more than a day's time to recover (it would be months for all of us). He was very apprehensive because he felt that he was disappointing the people he loved; he became anxious and irritable.

Consider this:

Don't be afraid to say, "Thank you, but maybe some other time," or "Thanks so much for thinking of me, but I'm going to have to take a rain check," or "I'm just not feeling up to going out to lunch today." Be gracious and appreciative, but if you don't want to do something, don't be afraid to say so.

Set your own limits, not those expected by others. I'm not suggesting that you do nothing on days when you have the energy to get out and be active. However, if you don't feel well, don't overdo it. Stand up for yourself by setting your own limits and not letting anyone interfere with your decision to not participate if you don't want to.

Chapter 12

Adopt a Forward-Thinking Attitude

Attitude is critical when dealing with any type of problem, especially a medical issue. It is no secret that your attitude can make a major difference in your recovery. I found myself in emotional peaks and valleys both before and after surgery. Some days I felt very positive and on top of the world; other days I found myself focusing on all of the negatives associated with my illness.

September 11, 2001, was a personal wake-up call for me. As I watched in horror at the events of the day on television, I realized that from that day on, my attitude deserved to be "forward-thinking" in memory of everyone who was impacted by the World Trade Center bombings.

Consider this:

Gaining a sense of control over what is happening to you will help with your attitude. Don't ever forget that you are loved and that there is someone or many people who are concerned about your health. You cannot change the past, but you can decide today that you are going to adopt a forward-thinking attitude. Here are some tips for doing just that:

- Look for the positives in the world—there is more positive than there is negative; it's all around us.

- Talk to yourself with *positive* self-talk.

- Limit your exposure to negative events on television which can be depressing.

- Surround yourself with positive people—those who will help you and not drag you down with their own problems and negativity.

- Avoid the people who stress you out simply because of the way that they view life.

Put your health problems in perspective. There are always people who have a worse situation than you do. I suspect that regardless of your health condition or your age (you do not have to be a senior to appreciate good health), that you know people who are dealing with more than you are right now. Count your blessings and pray for them.

Chapter 13

Try Not to Hurt the People You Love

A man who lost his wife summed it up by saying, "I loved her more than life itself, but when she found out that she was sick, she took it out on me. When she passed away, I felt a huge sense of loss, but I also felt relief because she was gone. During her illness, she was no longer the wonderful woman that I had married. I didn't know her anymore. Fortunately, I was able to forgive her and myself for hating her so."

On the plus side, illness can be a time for deepening your relationship with the people who care about you. It can mean a time for sharing your dreams as well as theirs. It can also be a time for discussing hopes and fears, as well

25

as love and appreciation for one another. Rejoice in the special things about your relationship. Listen to music together, enjoy a candlelight dinner, or simply hold each other. You don't have to do a lot of talking. Speak from your heart.

Consider this:

Recognize that family and friends, as well as health care professionals, are trying to help you. Sarcastic remarks, cruel comments, and hatred expressed through your verbal and non-verbal communication is hurtful, although not uncommon when people are sick. Do yourself and the people around you a favor and try not to hurt anyone because you are angry at your circumstances.

Many people are relieved when a friend or loved-one dies, not only because the pain is gone, but because the anger toward them (the caregiver) is also gone. Do not get yourself into that situation.

Think before you speak and act. Appreciate the people who are trying to help you. Show gratitude with a simple "thank you." If you cannot manage your emotions, seek professional help. This is a challenge, just as it was to accept your diagnosis. Work to overcome your negative emotions before you hurt the people you love.

Chapter 14

"It's Always Too Soon to Quit"

On April 28, 1993, Jim Valvano, the former coach of the North Carolina State University basketball team, passed away. Considered the underdog, Valvano and his team won the 1983 NCAA championship game. When he was diagnosed with cancer, he vowed to fight to overcome his illness just as he fought to win the championship.

Three years after his death, I found myself living through my personal illness by his words: "It's always too soon to quit." To this day I often think of his courage and the positive outlook he had on life. I had the opportunity to meet him twice at our company–sponsored pep rallies. He had a charismatic personality and a great sense of humor. He joked with our employees, signed autographs, and gave away basketballs, jackets, shirts, hats, and other memorabilia that our employees loved. He encouraged all of us to always give it our best shot.

When I found out from my neighbor that he was sick, I was devastated. How could this energetic man be struck down in the height of his career? The day he died his family, friends and the community lost an incredibly positive individual. He was a person who made this world a better place and left behind a very special legacy through his words.

Consider this:

When you're feeling low and discouraged and are ready to give up, remember the words of Jim Valvano. "When you quit, it's over. Don't give up. Never give up. It's always too soon to quit."

Chapter 15

Keep a Journal

There has been a lot of talk about "journaling" since Oprah Winfry encouraged millions of viewers to do just that. She has recorded in her personal journal since she was a young girl. Documenting your thoughts can help you deal with feelings of being overwhelmed, discouraged, frightened, and more. In addition, writing your thoughts down on paper can be very therapeutic.

I started my journal the day that I was diagnosed and recorded anywhere from a few sentences to several pages four to five times each week. Doing so helped me to get through some pretty rough days. I wrote about anything and everything that popped into my mind including my fears and frustration. At times I felt like I was talking to a secret friend who truly understood my anxiety. In reality, my journal did become my friend and remains my friend today.

Consider this:

Get started. You can make entries in your journal every day or as you desire. Write using a computer or do so by hand in a fancy book or simply on a tablet of paper. Make time to write. Don't re-read what you have written too soon. Give it time so that when you do re-read your journal, you will be able to see how much progress you have made both physically and mentally. I believe that if you try "journaling" you will enjoy it. You may even find yourself looking forward to the time in your day or week that you have set-aside in your mind for this special healing exercise.

Chapter 16

Listen to Your Intuition

Some people seem to be naturally more intuitive than others, but we all have a sense of what feels right or wrong. Since my tumor experience, I find myself making a special effort to listen to my intuition. If something does not feel quite right, I usually get it checked out. Do not let fear interfere with what your intuition is telling you.

Several years ago I attended Emory University's Mini-Medical School for lay people. One of the things that I remember most about the eight-week long class is that we were told that patients often know what is wrong with them, or at least have a strong suspicion. Their medical students are encouraged to ask their patients, "What do you think the problem might be?" I can identify with that technique because I believe that many times our intuition does enlighten us in this way.

Consider this:

Initially, I ignored my gradual hearing loss and slight dizziness. An ear, nose and throat (ENT) doctor suggested that a virus had probably attacked my auditory nerve and caused my hearing to deteriorate. In the back of my mind I knew that something was wrong, but in spite of my anxious feelings I chose to ignore my intuition. I didn't immediately act on my feelings and pursue another medical opinion. As an active woman with a business to run, people to see, and places to go to, I didn't have time to be sick. My outcome was favorable, but the delay in getting an accurate diagnosis resulted in a more complex and risky treatment.

If you think there is something wrong, do not be afraid to see a doctor. Most illnesses are treatable in their early stages. When we ignore warning signs, we sometimes get ourselves into trouble.

Chapter 17

Allow Yourself a "Time-Out"

Beyond taking care of YOU, there may be times when you simply need to stop what you are doing and DO NOTHING. One of my favorite time-out activities is walking at the mall before the mall opens at 10 a.m. I simply enjoy power walking past the storefronts with the wonderful fragrances drifting under the security gates of *Victoria's Secret*, and *Bath & Body Works*. I often see the same people every morning. For me it is a relaxing "time-out" that I enjoy to this day.

Riding my bicycle in the spring and fall when the weather is perfect for "sight-seeing" in the neighborhood is something I especially enjoy doing. Another favorite pastime is boating. When I come back from an afternoon at the lake, I feel like I have been gone for the entire weekend. If I get a chance to water-ski that's even better. These time-outs keep me energized.

Consider this:

Trying to keep up with daily responsibilities can be exhausting and in many cases unnecessary. Don't worry about having a house that is in tip-top shape, or a lawn that is edged and free of weeds, or kids that are squeaky clean. These expectations are unrealistic, especially when you're sick. So what if you need a haircut, or the car needs washing, or the garage needs organizing? It can wait until you feel better. Don't push yourself too hard.

Take a nap when you are tired. Excuse yourself from a volunteer obligation if you are not feeling up to it. Relax with friends. Take a sick day off from work. Sit in your yard and enjoy the natural beauty that surrounds you. Feed the squirrels and chipmunks. Look for ways to take time-outs.

Chapter 18

Watch Your Diet

Sometimes when we are sick, we tend to eat anything and everything that tastes good regardless of the fact that some of it is just plain junk! If you have never been interested in healthy eating, this might be a good time to start. Because of your physical condition, your body may need more calories, vitamins, minerals and protein than you normally eat. The U.S. Food and Drug Administration (FDA) has determined consumption levels for vitamins and calls it "daily allowances." If you do not get enough from food, you may need supplements and higher than normal amounts of nutrients.

Resist the temptation to eat unhealthy foods because you just don't care what happens to you anymore. That kind of thinking is counter-productive and can lead to malnutrition or at the very least, bad eating habits that can be difficult to reverse later on.

Consider this:

Water, carbohydrates, proteins and fats are the foundation of a healthy diet. Speak to your doctor about your diet if you have questions regarding what you should and should not be eating. Your doctor may even refer you to a dietician for additional help in planning menus. Fruits, vegetables, protein, fiber, and fat should be part of your regular eating habits. Work at maintaining a well-balanced diet appropriate for you.

On the other hand, "belly stuffers" do just that. They fill your stomach, provide nothing of value, and are waste of money despite the fact that they may taste good to you. If you enjoy junk food, try eating it in moderation. My worst eating period was during the time that I was on steroids. I ate everything in sight and soon regained the weight that I had lost.

Get your entire household to share with you in your commitment to healthy eating. It is so much easier to eat right if the others at your table want to do the same. You might even try experimenting in the kitchen with new foods and recipes. It is more fun when everyone jumps on the bandwagon and joins in the joy of cooking and good nutrition.

Chapter 19

Consider a Holistic
Approach to Healing

When I was diagnosed I immediately looked to cures other than the dreaded surgery. My tumor was "slow growing" so I was able to take my time up to a point. I recognize that everyone is not in the same situation. I decided to try the holistic approach as well as alternative medicine as a complement to more traditional medicine.

When I think of holistic and alternative medicine and healing I think about the whole person, both mental and spiritual. I also think about vegetarianism, peppermint and chamomile teas, aromatherapy, hypnosis, high doses of vitamins, acupuncture, chiropractors, reflexology, herbs and unusual treatments with substances I have never heard of such as shark cartilage capsules. I tried that too in an attempt to kill my tumor. Unfortunately, it didn't work.

I also tried hypnosis in an attempt to mentally shrink the tumor. It did not work either, but I found that I was very easily hypnotized (no doubt because I was totally open to the idea in the hope that it would help me). It was a new and relaxing experience for me, and I am glad that I tried it.

There are many avenues under the holistic and alternative medicine "umbrellas." It may take some extra research, but it can be worth the effort if you eventually find what you are looking for in the way of options.

Consider this:

Despite the fact that there is some quackery out there, practitioners who have a holistic and alternative focus and who genuinely have something to offer are abundant. In addition, there are a number of good books on this subject including those by two of my favorite authors, Andrew Weil, M.D. and Bernie Siegel, M.D. I recommend reading as much as you can to learn whether or not a holistic approach to healing might be helpful to you.

In addition, many doctors do not know much about what some might label, "divergent medicine." Some wish they knew more. Others are skeptical enough to avoid prescribing herbal treatments and unusual or "wacky" approaches to healing. In addition, some doctors who are in favor of alternative and holistic medicine may be overly cautious when using nontraditional remedies. Find the doctor who can meet your needs.

If you would like to try herbs and your physician is not particularly familiar with herbal treatments, look at the following web site www.quackwatch.org. It will help you determine whether or not the herb is safe and effective.

The future of medicine seems to be integrative in that it considers the mind, body and spirit. It is the best of alternative and traditional medicine combined. There are certainly many years of research and studies ahead of us, but for now, a holistic approach to healing might just be what you're looking for.

Chapter 20

Take a "Good News" Inventory

For some people, looking for the "good news" is not particular easy to do. When we feel down, it becomes easier to focus on what we do not have—how lousy life is treating us. We may look into the mirror and see a face we hardly recognize—one ravaged by pain and chemotherapy, radiation and stress. Who wouldn't want to focus on the worst? However, doing so will not improve your situation.

During my illness I concentrated on reminding myself how good I really had it. My brain tumor was benign, not malignant. I had a wonderful support system of family and friends who loved me unconditionally. At times it was difficult to concentrate on the positives in my life, but I forced myself to do it. I repeated the phrase "Focus on what you have, not on what you don't have" dozens of times throughout the day. When I woke up in the middle of the night and could not sleep because I was worried about what was going to become of me, I thought about all of the positive things in my life.

I eventually took an inventory and compiled a "have" list of things for which I was grateful. My list grew longer each day and included things like family and many friends, two cats whom I adore, the ability to eat, see, speak, hear, walk and drive a car. My list grew to three pages. I copied my list and posted it in my home office and bathroom. I still carry it with me in my purse today. Every time I get discouraged I read my "good news" inventory. Doing so even when I'm already having a great day is the icing on the cake!

Consider this:

You can do the same. Make a list of the blessings in your life. Start with the people you care about. Follow with everything else positive that comes to mind. You can easily do what I did. Just pick up a pen and start writing or turn on your computer and start typing. All it takes is a mental commitment and a refusal to allow yourself to get stuck on the negative side of illness. Begin today by making a list of the positives in your life. I'd be willing to bet that your list will meet or exceed mine if you are open to putting a little effort into it.

Chapter 21

Laughter is Great Medicine

When my friend was bedridden for months, she missed laughter more than food, friendship, or even her favorite television programs that she did not have the energy to watch. She wanted more than anything to laugh, hear a joke or be told a funny story. When she felt better I rented Bill Cosby's videos because he was her favorite comedian. When she had seen everything he had to offer, I went back to the comedy section at the video store and checked out dozens of other videos that not only made her laugh, but also helped her to heal from the inside out. *Vacation*, *European Vacation* and *Christmas Vacation* were three of her all-time favorite movies, mostly because she loved Chevy Chase. She literally laughed her way back to health.

Consider this:

What makes you laugh? Is it a friend with a great sense of humor or something else? Do you ever listen to the crazy disc jockeys on the radio talk programs? Do you have a favorite game show or television serial that tickles your funny bone? Have you ever read a book of jokes?

Remember Erma Bombeck? She was a very funny lady who entertained us on stage as well as through her writing. She found humor in everyday situations. I believe that there is an Erma Bombeck in all of us. Find a way to bring some humor into your life. Laughter may be the best medicine or at the very least, a tonic for temporary relief from the stress of your diagnosis.

There is also an interesting web site that is worth mentioning. It offers popular syndicated comics such as *For Better or For Worse*, *Cathy*, and *Calvin and Hobbes* as well as editorial cartoons and games. You can check it out at www.ucomics.com. Another great site is *Laughter Heals Foundation* at laughterheals.org. This web site was launched by Craig Shoemaker to bring more laughs to hospitals and physical rehabilitation centers.

Chapter 22

Expect Your Fear to Return

As you try to put your surgery or treatment behind you, you may find it difficult to forget the details of your experience. I occasionally still struggle with thoughts of the tumor growing back even though I have regular MRIs to make sure that there is no problem. I know a number of people for whom tumor re-growth has become a reality, so I am justifiably concerned. Some of my friends for whom chemotherapy and radiation was a nightmare are stressed-out and worry about a recurrence of cancer.

It is not uncommon for fear to return especially late at night when you are lying in bed. Negative thoughts can quickly force positive thoughts out of the way at any time and before you know it, you are focusing on old fears.

Consider this:

You may have to work at it, but you can put fearful thoughts out of your mind. Take a stand and refuse to let your fear consume you. Force yourself to look toward the future. Do not get stuck thinking too much about the past unless to do so will mentally help you transition to present-day.

My worst memory of my tumor surgery was lying in the intensive care unit for forty-eight hours. My head hurt, and I was SO thirsty! I could never have imagined that I could feel so crummy. However, I constantly reminded myself that every day I would improve and that I would feel 100 percent better. And guess what? I did feel better every day. Now when I find myself thinking about my ICU experience, I quickly push those depressing thoughts out of my head because they interfere with my enjoyment of the present.

And speaking of the present, if you have not read the book, *The Precious Present* by Spencer Johnson, I highly recommend it. This book is short and to the point. It offers a powerful message of faith, hope, love and the secret to personal happiness.

Chapter 23

Disability Doesn't Mean Not Being Able to Do Something

If you find yourself in a situation in which you have become disabled, don't think that it means that you cannot do the things you have done in the past. That is not necessarily the case for many people. It may just mean finding a *different* way to do the things you used to do.

For example, my tumor buddy, Sandy, is a runner. She has run dozens of marathons both before and after her surgery. Post-surgery she is a bit off-balance due to the cut balance nerve, but she is still able to run and does not worry as much about her "time." She sometimes has to stop during the race to rest, but she refuses to give up doing what she loves to do.

Here is another example: At times my one-sided deafness is annoying to me as well as to others to whom I must ask to repeat what they said. I find it especially challenging when I am speaking before a room filled with hundreds of people. Although they can hear me because of my microphone, I often can't hear them when they ask a question. I cannot even determine who in the room has asked the question because I am unable to tell where the sound is coming from. I walk toward the audience, find the individual that spoke and hand him or her a microphone. Only then can I, as well as the audience, hear what is being said. I also compensate by reading lips, something that came naturally as I gradually lost my hearing due to the growth of the tumor.

Consider this:

If you have a disability, do not let it hold you back. Find another way to do the things that you enjoy. Some disabilities are "invisible" while others are apparent. Regardless of what type of disability you may have, resolve to not let it interfere with your life and the things you like to do.

Getting cancer was "...the best thing that ever happened to me."

—Lance Armstrong

PART TWO

PART TWO has a total of thirteen chapters, all of which offer ideas to help you make decisions about your treatment. However, keep in mind that I am not trying to provide medical advice. I am not a doctor, but merely speak from my personal experience as a patient. Here are the action steps that you might want to consider taking to address the day to day challenges of dealing with your illness.

PART TWO opens with Chapter 24 which is called *Get a 2nd, 3rd 4th Opinion*. I am a strong advocate of second opinions, especially if you are not satisfied with what you are hearing or feel you are not getting the complete story. I encourage you to never give up, even if the medical experts do not know what is wrong with you. With today's rapid medical advances, it may take extra effort to find the best treatment options for you.

This part continues with chapters such as *Insist on Understanding, Clarify What Will be Done,* and *Guard Against Medical Errors, Check Out the Hospital and Express Your Gratitude.* Each of the chapters in PART TWO were carefully written with the patient reader in mind. I tried to include everything that I personally found helpful and that I believe that you will also.

I hope that you find this part of the book practical, uplifting and exactly what you need to move forward on your journey.

Chapter 24

Get a 2nd, 3rd, 4th Opinion

As I mentioned in a preceding chapter, I'm an advocate of getting additional opinions. One person's opinion is just that, one person's opinion. It may or may not be the right way to proceed in helping you. In some situations, diagnosis is difficult, but necessary if you are going to get to the cause and best method of treatment for your problem. I have always been amazed at how many people will accept the idea that the doctor knows there is something wrong, but does not know what the problem is and tells the patient to just "live with it."

If you watch television or read the newspapers, you are aware of situations where patients have been misdiagnosed or a surgery was performed that was not necessary. For instance, a woman with breast cancer was told she did not have cancer. Her symptoms persisted and three months later another doctor, who was immediately suspicious and ordered the necessary tests, diagnosed her. It was not good news, but the cancer was caught early enough to treat successfully. Had the patient given up despite her discomfort, she may not have survived her illness.

In another example, Ed's wife, Kathryn, was seriously ill. They were determined to find out what was causing her seizures and how she could best be treated. They met with more than twenty doctors before a doctor correctly identified her problem along with a cure. They refused to give up until they found someone who could help her. How many people would be that persistent?

Consider this:

Although consulting that many doctors is unusual, it points to the importance of getting more than one opinion. This is especially critical when the illness is difficult to diagnose or multiple treatment options exist. Don't give up. Accepting the opinion or advice of one individual could cost you your life.

On the other hand, time is important and you may not have a lot of time to see a dozen doctors or more. Get organized and do what you can to get an accurate perspective on your situation. Be particularly diligent in getting another opinion if the treatment being suggested is invasive, is especially expensive, or has the reputation for being overdone such as back surgery, gallbladder removal, cataract surgery, or hysterectomy.

Lastly, carefully evaluate the expertise and biases of the health care professionals that you see. In addition, when you seek a second opinion, do not go to doctors who are professionally connected with the doctor who diagnosed you. Most doctors are reluctant to contradict a colleague that is in the same group practice.

Chapter 25

Prepare to Ask Questions

Doctors and medical professionals are busy people. They appreciate patients who are organized and well informed. Most do not have the time or an interest in listening to people who ramble and don't know what they want to say. Does this sound like you? If so, you need a plan. It does not have to be anything elaborate—handwritten notes will do as long as you take them with you to your doctor's appointment and are not afraid to ask. List them in order of importance. You are paying for your appointment and you deserve to get answers to your questions.

Consider this:

Prior to meeting with your doctor, make a list of the questions that you want to have answered along with specific information you feel the doctor should know about you. Your questions should be written or typed on a separate sheet of paper. Your questions might include:

Regarding treatment/surgery

- What are the treatment options?
- Can the treatment wait? How long?
- What will happen if I don't have treatment?

- What are the diagnostic options and accuracy of the tests?
- Where are the centers of expertise for my problem?
- How long have you been performing treatment of this nature?
- What kinds of complications have your patients had?
- Will a team of doctors or just you do the surgery?
- How long will the surgery take?
- Am I a candidate for local anesthesia versus general anesthesia?
- How many days will I be in the hospital?
- How much discomfort will I have and how will it be managed?
- What follow-up procedures may be required or are likely to be required?
- What questions should I be asking that I don't know I should be asking?
- Will my health insurance cover the costs of the treatment/surgery?

Regarding medications

- What is the medication for?
- How often should I take it and at what time of the day?
- Should I take it on an empty or full stomach?
- Can I take it with other medications that I am already taking?
- What side effects are likely?
- What should I do if I have side effects?
- What are the long-term risks of being on this medication?
- How and when will I know if the medication is working?

- Are there generic or less costly alternatives?
- Do you offer samples of the medication?

Chapter 26

Take Along a Tape Recorder

So much is said in the medical setting to patients that it can quickly become overwhelming. Lots of questions are asked, diagnostic tests may be reviewed or scheduled, prescriptions are dispensed and instructions are given that they may not be understood or remembered.

Your own emotional involvement can interfere with a thorough analysis and developing understanding. If you have ever been in this situation, you know exactly what I mean. I personally found it invaluable to have a friend with me to take notes and ask the questions that I did not think to ask. When I was alone, I took along a tape recorder.

Consider this:

You should not feel the least bit uncomfortable with a tape recorder. Ask permission from the doctor to record what he or she says with the understanding that the recording is for your personal use only. Your goal is to make sure that you walk out of the doctor's office with a complete knowledge of what has been said to you.

If you would rather take a family member or a friend with you, that can work too. You need to focus on asking questions and listening to what is being said. You should not have to worry about whether or not you will remember the details later. Even taking notes can interfere with your ability to comprehend, especially if you are under a lot of stress.

Chapter 27

Insist on Understanding

Whether knowingly or unknowingly, doctors sometimes intimidate their patients. The patient may then fail to get a clear understanding of what is happening to him or her. Doctors often use medical terminology that is confusing to a lay person. This is another good reason to take your caregiver with you when you meet with your doctor(s).

I had several opinions (7 to be exact) and from that experience I found that some physicians communicated more clearly than others. Although I knew a lot about my tumor treatment options because of my research, there were several times when I did not understand and had to ask for clarification. I never hesitated to ask questions. In fact, I was encouraged by my doctors to take my time and ask all of the questions that I wanted to ask. In one case that meant a lot to me, as I inevitably had to wait more than two hours beyond my appointment time to see the doctor.

On another occasion the doctor drew a sketch of the anatomy of my brain with a tumor occupying valuable space in my head. In two other situations the doctors put my MRI films on a lighted screen and pointed out the location of my tumor. They also explained in great detail the significance of the tumor and how it would gradually rob me of my ability to function.

In any event, I knew it was important to insist on understanding. I never once left a doctor's office without comprehending what I had been told. I knew that unless I spoke up, the doctor would assume that I fully understood what was discussed.

Consider this:

Your list of questions will help you to clarify those things that are unclear. However, do not be embarrassed to probe further until you are satisfied with what you are hearing. If you have the time prior to your doctor's visit, research your illness and treatment alternatives. Doctors appreciate patients who understand their situations and ask intelligent questions. See Chapter 25 (Prepare to Ask Questions) for a list of samples.

Chapter 28

Tell Your Doctor the Truth

You may be tempted to withhold information from your doctor or lie to avoid hearing bad news. At the very least, you may downplay your illness because you are afraid that what you are about to reveal could generate information that you don't want to hear.

For example, Ellen did not share the fact that she had rectal bleeding for almost a year even when she met with her doctor for her annual physical. Later she developed abdominal pain and sought advice from her gynecologist. He referred Ellen back to her internist. The internist ordered a colonoscopy and discovered that she had colon cancer. Surgery followed immediately upon diagnosis and Ellen is now recovering, but she almost lost her life because she didn't tell her doctor the truth when she had a hunch that something was wrong.

Consider this:

Open dialogue is the foundation for a good doctor-patient relationship. Whether you are discussing sexually transmitted diseases or how much alcohol you drink, you need to be honest for your own benefit. Doctors have heard it all, and you are not going to embarrass them by fully disclosing your medical history and/or concerns. The

51

doctor is not a police officer, but is there to help you. That's what you are paying for.

In addition, some medications and vitamins can interfere with other medications or treatments. Herbal supplements can even work against you before surgery as they may interfere with blood clotting and intensify the effects of anesthetics. Your doctor needs to know about these things too.

In summary, even if you think what you want to discuss is unimportant, if it concerns your health you need to mention it to the doctor. If you have a preference concerning medication or method of treatment, say so. Your doctor is not a mind reader.

Chapter 29

What if You Are a Medical Mystery?

Sometimes bad news is shrouded in mystery because the doctor truly doesn't know what's wrong with you, but feels you definitely have a problem. Some doctors are better at diagnosing than others. However, no diagnosis is often as bad as knowing what the problem is.

For example, James was told following a chest x-ray that the results showed an abnormality. However, the doctor did not know what the problem might be. He told him not to worry, but to come back in six months. James left the doctor's office frightened and confused.

However, he didn't wait six months to seek a second opinion. Further testing revealed scar tissue from a past pneumonia; he was immediately relieved. His intuition told him that he needed an appointment with another doctor for further evaluation and that's what he did.

Consider this:

If you believe that you are a medical mystery (the doctor doesn't know what's wrong with you), get another opinion. Ideally, you will want to find a specialist who has the time and interest to invest in your case. He or she will probably run some tests. If the specialist cannot determine the problem, keep looking until you find someone who can. Doctors cannot possibly make the correct diagnosis every time. They have limitations just as you do.

On another note, rather than running from doctor to doctor, you may be tempted to give up and accept a vague diagnosis and pretend nothing is wrong just because it is a hassle to keep searching for an answer. That decision could be fatal. You have only one life. You owe it to yourself to go sleuthing in order to get the answers you need to make an informed decision regarding your treatment plan if one is needed.

Chapter 30

Clarify What Will Be Done

Any procedure or surgery can seem terrifying unless you are the doctor who has done it thousands of times. It is your responsibility to make sure that you understand what will be happening to you. There are even some things you can do to help avoid a mistake.

For example, immediately prior to my surgery, my friend Sue, who is a nurse, and who accompanied me to California, drew a heart on my cheek with lipstick on the side where the tumor was located. There was no second-guessing in the operating room about which side of my head had the tumor.

I also knew what to expect when I woke up. I was told that my head would be bandaged turban-style, and that painkillers would be readily available to me. The doctor told me that I would have a catheter, and that I would not be able to get up and move around until I was transferred from ICU to a private room approximately two days later. I felt a lot more comfortable as I was wheeled into the operating room knowing what I could expect after surgery.

Consider this:

If you are having surgery or a medical procedure, make sure that your primary care physician and your surgeon know exactly what will be done and that they explain it to you. Do not leave anything to chance. Informed patients take responsibility for what is about to happen to them. If you are unable to make decisions for yourself, be sure that a reliable and capable individual is there to look out for your best interests.

Chapter 31

Don't Be Talked Into Something

Prompt medical treatment saves lives, but speed can also take or permanently destroy lives. Most of us are pretty stressed-out when the doctor has bad news, but hastily jumping into a surgery or treatment that may be irreversible is not a good idea. On the other hand, delaying the inevitable can be risky business. Your solution to the dilemma lies in obtaining enough information to make an informed decision in the time that you have available.

You may find it tempting to accept what your first opinion has to say simply because it means you don't have to make more appointments to see additional doctors. However, if you feel that you are being talked into something, you owe it to yourself to explore other options.

Consider this:

Take a couple of days or even weeks if time allows so that you can decide what you are going to do. A desire to quickly get it all over with can lead to a regrettable decision that doesn't have to happen. Finally, do not let anyone push you into something of which you are unsure. Expediency can save lives, but it is a fact that thousands of unnecessary surgeries are performed every year—surgeries that could have been replaced with a more conservative treatment approach.

Chapter 32

Check Out the Hospital

Make sure that you are comfortable with not only the doctors who are treating you, but also with the hospital or outpatient facility that will care for you. Just because a hospital is close to your home does not mean it is a good choice unless the medical team has substantial experience treating people with your health condition. For example, the hospital in a small community may be fine for routine surgeries, but not for more complicated procedures such as coronary artery by-pass or transplant surgery.

Consider this:

Contact the hospital and ask for the Medical Director's office. They should have statistics on how often they have treated people with your condition. You may have to travel fifty, five hundred or more miles to get the best medical care available. Find the top facility or you may run a higher risk of a negative outcome; it's that simple.

I traveled several thousand miles because the hospital and the doctors were among the best in the world for the surgery and follow-up care that I needed. This was not a difficult decision. It was definitely the right thing for me despite having to fly across the country and back.

Chapter 33

Keep Track of Your Records

Medical records including lab tests, x-rays, ultrasounds, MRI reports, CT scans, etc., are important. Therefore, it is to your benefit to have a simple system for keeping track of your vital health information. Doctors cannot possibly be central record keepers for their patients. The days of family doctors who know everything about their patients are long gone. In addition, doctors see so many people that it is nearly impossible to prevent records from getting lost. But what can a patient do about it?

Consider this:

You may want to keep copies of the results of routine or preventive physical, dental and vision exams in your possession. You may also want to keep copies of reports from various diagnostic procedures and tests, especially those that relate to your immediate medical concern (e.g., EKG, stress test, mammogram, PSA test, CT films, MRI films, biopsies, colonoscopy, ultrasound, blood tests, and x-rays).

You may have to make some phone calls and sign a "release of medical information" form to get all of this data, but it is imperative that you do so. You will want to take these reports to discuss with your doctor(s). Once shared, the doctor may decide to re-run some or all of the tests. The first set of tests is often used for comparison with those that follow. It is also handy to have them in the event that you end up in an emergency room.

I actually had two sets of my most recent MRI reports because I had more than one doctor evaluating them simultaneously. After a long-distance consultation, most doctors will mail your films back to you; however, some will not. Ask what the policy is before you send anything. In addition, some test results can be put on a CD.

Test results can easily get lost. And if they do, it is expensive to replace them as well as time-consuming, even if you do not have to be re-tested. A copy of MRI or CT films is something you will want to keep in a safe place at home. I have a three-ring binder for the actual written reports, and I keep the films in the labeled jackets in which they came.

Keep track of your medical records in an organized manner. I carry a short list with me that includes:

- Insurance carrier information
- Doctors' contact information
- Medications
- My blood type
- Allergies

I felt much better knowing that I had this information at my fingertips when I needed it. I found it frustrating when I requested that MRI films be mailed to another doctor, and it took six weeks for the films to be sent. As a result, my most recent films could not be immediately compared to the previous films.

Chapter 34

Guard Against Medical Errors

Anyone who reads the newspaper or watches television knows that medical errors can cause irreversible situations including death. I found this out first hand when I was hospitalized in Atlanta. My tumor caused hydrocephalus that required the installation of a brain shunt. This took place six months prior to the surgery to remove the tumor in California.

The shunt surgery went smoothly, but I woke up vomiting at midnight and called for a nurse. A nurse's aide responded and said she would contact my nurse about giving me some medication. The nurse did not check on me until 4:30 a.m. When I asked her if she had gotten my message she replied: "Oh my god. I gave your shot to the woman in the room next door to you!" She thought it was funny and started laughing. I was speechless and decided that I would leave the hospital that morning if I had to run out of there naked!

To this day I wonder what happened to the woman in the room next to mine after she was given my shot. Before I checked out, a beautiful floral arrangement that had been sent to me by a client was delivered to her room.

Consider this:

After that, I vowed that I would never be alone overnight in a hospital again. I truly believe that every patient needs an advocate—someone, who will look out for his or her best interests, especially when the patient is unable to do so. Hospitals are busy places and mistakes can happen.

For example, if you are scheduled for surgery, ensure that the site of the impending operation is clearly marked. Question every medication you are given, especially if it is different than the previous one given to you. Make sure that your hospital food matches your dietary needs or restrictions. For example, if you are diabetic, you know what to eat and what not to eat. Your caregiver should go to bat for you if you are unable to communicate effectively.

On another note, when your doctor gives you a prescription, make sure that you can read his or her handwriting. If you cannot, the pharmacist may not be able to read it either. Ask that the name of the medication be printed on the prescription or on a separate piece of paper along with the dosage and how often it should be taken.

Chapter 35

Express Your Gratitude

My mother was a registered nurse. At times she felt that it was a thankless job. She said that despite the fact that she had saved many lives during her 40-year career, she could count on one hand the number of patients who personally thanked her. She made a point of thanking everyone on a daily basis when she was hospitalized. She also gave the medical team a five-pound box of fine chocolates when she checked out.

Expressing gratitude costs nothing, but it can make a difference in how others react to you. Although we might like to believe that everyone is treated the same when it comes to medical care, that kind of thinking is unrealistic. Patients who show sincere appreciation will be treated differently from those who neglect to do so or who are rude to the nurses, technicians, and doctors. You can bet on it!

Consider this:

There is no substitute for the words "Thank you." Health care professionals are over-worked and in many cases, underpaid. Why do these people continue to do what they do? You would have to ask them. The response I got in an interview with a nurse was this, "I enjoy helping people; it gives me the kind of personal satisfaction that I can't get in any other type of work." When probed further, she admitted that expressions of gratitude on behalf of her patients are often few and far between. "They aren't feeling well and seem to take for granted the things we do for them. It's unfortunate, but true."

Don't forget to let the people who help you know how much you appreciate what they are doing for you. You will stand out in their minds and may even find that your medical care is better than the norm as a result.

Chapter 36

Prepare to Leave the Hospital

If your illness requires a hospital stay, you will eventually be discharged. There is no place like home and nothing beats sleeping in your own bed! The noise level in a hospital can be enough to drive some patients crazy. The lack of privacy can also be upsetting. Bedpans, IVs, and hospital gowns are no fun. Neither is hospital food in most institutions. Either there is not enough of it, it's tasteless, or it's just plain boring.

It was music to my ears when my doctor said, "Would you like to go home?" Saying that I wanted to leave would have been a gross understatement! Despite the wonderful care that I had received, I was ready to get out of there. Unfortunately in my case, home meant a week at the guest center on the hospital campus since I live in Atlanta, and my surgery was in Los Angeles. It would be another week, plus an eye surgery to implant a wire spring into my eyelid, before I really got to go "home."

Consider this:

Prior to entering the hospital, start planning for your release. You may not be in the best shape to ask questions and make decisions when you are getting ready to leave; that is why it makes sense to plan ahead. Prepare a list of questions that you anticipate asking your doctor *before* you are discharged. If you are not able to ask, your caregiver should be able to take over. Questions might include:

- What, if any, medications will I be taking?
- What are the potential side effects of the medication(s)?
- What food, drink (including alcohol) or activities should I avoid when taking this medication?
- How often will my bandages need to be changed?
- When can I take a shower/bath?
- Will a dietician explain dietary needs?
- How soon can I start exercising, and what type of exercise is permissible?

- When is my first follow-up office appointment with you?
- What potential problems may occur and what should I do?

These are a few of the questions that I would be asking upon leaving the hospital. It is easier to get answers to these questions when you have got the doctor's attention than if you call his or her office and are referred to an assistant. Assistants can be very helpful, but I prefer speaking directly to the doctor whenever possible.

"Courage is contagious. When a brave person takes a stand, the spines of others are stiffened."

—*Reverend Billy Graham*

PART THREE

PART THREE includes chapters that encompass ideas that I believe you will find helpful. From *Take Care of YOU* through *Let Go of the Game Plan*, PART THREE is loaded with positive energy and suggestions for making the period of time during which you are ill, easier and more comfortable.

I view life as an accumulation of gifts; life is a gift that was given to us by someone other than ourselves. I personally felt an obligation to my wonderful parents to fight for my life and keep on living, especially now that they are gone. My father always said, "Honey, don't ever forget that life is for the living." His words echo in my mind more than ever today.

Do whatever it takes to help yourself focus on all of the reasons you have for not giving up. What are you passionate about? Examine the relationships you have with the people in your life, especially with your family. Inventory your unfulfilled dreams. What else would you like to do during your lifetime? Write about these things in your journal or simply keep a list for handy reference, as does my friend Mary Ann.

She decided after her diagnosis of impending blindness that she had a lot of living to do. She wrote down everything that came to mind that she wanted to accomplish in her lifetime. She immediately got started with a trip to France to see the Eiffel Tower.

I sincerely hope that the ideas in PART THREE will help you to keep on living for yourself and for those who love and have loved you. I have included a variety of uplifting, but practical ideas that I believe you will find helpful beginning with *Develop a Menu of Mood-Boosting Techniques.*

Chapter 37

Develop a Menu of
Mood-Boosting Techniques

We all have times when we feel mentally down, especially if our treatment plan is not working as we had anticipated. The mind is flexible and open to stimulus that can help us deal with our emotional feelings on a day to day basis if we let it. I personally found a menu of mood-boosting techniques helpful in keeping me on track and in a positive frame of mind during my illness. I have tried to include in the following list some things that you can do even if you are confined to bed.

Consider this:

Try some of these mood-boosting techniques:

- Eat breakfast in bed
- Listen to your favorite music
- Go to a ball game
- Take a bubble bath
- Use aromatherapy on your pillows
- Ask a friend or loved one to read to you
- Listen to books on audio-tape
- Enjoy the moment with a bouquet of fresh flowers
- Watch an old movie on television

- Get your hair cut or change the style and/or color
- Go for a ride in the country
- Treat yourself to a massage or facial
- Go for a walk in a park
- Have a cup of coffee or lunch with a friend
- Attend a church service
- Shop for a new "something"
- Play with your pet
- Join a chat room on the Internet
- Visit your grandchildren
- Plant some flowers
- Read Scriptures from the Bible
- Express gratitude to a loved one
- Enjoy a back rub
- Play a board game with a group of friends
- Go on a picnic
- Read a book of poetry
- Ride a horse
- Feed a baby
- Do anything that makes you feel better about yourself

Chapter 38

Don't Let Your Inner Happiness Depend on Outer Circumstances

I know a number of people whose inner happiness depends upon what is going on around them. While not clinically depressed, unless certain things are taking place outside of their minds, they are sad. I find it difficult to understand, but I know that some people truly rely on others, or either their work or their recreation to keep themselves happy.

Bryan is an example of this. He was diagnosed with prostate cancer in the earliest stage. He is what I would call a "morale buster" kind of personality. He is never fun to be around and now that he has a life-threatening illness, he is very difficult to live with, at least that's what his wife says. He has always gotten his kicks and happiness in life from outward circumstances. When he does not have access to those things, he is down in the dumps and he makes everyone around him miserable.

Consider this:

Find a way to enjoy your own company. Being sick is not fun, but the strength you carry within you may only need to be tapped. It is a resource that is there if you want to take advantage of it. Solitary time to read a book, see a movie, or have a cup of coffee at your favorite coffee shop, may be just what you need to perk yourself up.

Your inner happiness has a lot to do with attitude and the way in which you face adversity. Your spirit is stronger than you realize. "Happiness," said Benjamin Franklin, "is produced not so much by great pieces of good fortune that seldom happen as by little advantages that occur every day." Take time to enjoy the day's magic moments.

Chapter 39

See the Big Picture

At some point in our life, most of us will be faced with health-related issues of one kind or another. It might be something as simple as a cracked tooth that requires a crown. I use the word "simple," but to anyone who has never cracked a tooth that required a crown, the thought is frightening, just like having a biopsy is to anyone who has never had the procedure.

Typically, our lives are filled with a number of minor or major medical crises, which we survive and put behind us. In all probability each medical crisis we face will result in our continued ability to live a productive and satisfying life. So, facing a biopsy might be viewed as just another "speed bump" in life. Try to put things in perspective.

Consider this:

Keep looking at what you are going through as part of the grand scheme of life. Life presents us with hurdles of all sizes and types. A cracked tooth or broken toe could have been much worse. Even brain tumor surgery that was very scary could have been more difficult than it was. Today, when people ask me how I am doing despite the fact that I still have some physical problems, I respond with, "Great!"

71

In my heart, I have come to terms with what has changed for me, and the fact that I will never be the same person I once was. I grieved the loss of my old self and have finally accepted who I am today. I have been able to move forward with plans for the rest of my life. I continue to keep the big picture on my radar screen.

Chapter 40

Set Short-Term Goals

Short-term goals have given me an effective way to deal with illness and recovery. Looking too far into the future at the amount of time required to work through an illness can be overwhelming. When you are worried about tomorrow and beyond, it can be difficult to get anything accomplished today, much less feel better.

For example, I was told that I might be out of work for up to six months because the type of surgery that I had can be very disruptive to the entire body. I was also told that I might be more tired than normal, although by the time I had surgery I had forgotten what "normal" was.

I was encouraged by the hospital staff to participate in a rehabilitation program to help improve my balance since my balance nerve on one side had been severed during surgery (something I knew would occur). I also knew for sure that I would need facial re-animation therapy to help get my paralyzed face moving again. Thinking about all of this made me anxious, but I knew that there had to be a way to tame those feelings; I started looking for solutions.

To help me transition to normal physical activity, I set a goal to start taking short walks on a daily basis one week after my release from the hospital. My next short-term goal was to be able to walk three miles within three weeks of my surgery. After six weeks I wanted to be back to working out at the YMCA one hour every other day. As a result of setting short-term goals, I was back to my pre-surgery activity level in less than two months rather than six months as predicted.

Consider this:

Pace yourself. Set short-term goals and then celebrate when you reach those goals. Treat yourself to something you especially enjoy when you hit the first short-term milestone. You've heard the expression: "Rome wasn't built in a day." Your recovery may not happen overnight or within a few days, or even a few weeks. It may take you months or years to get totally back on your feet depending upon what you need to do to get there.

You may be facing numerous challenges during your recovery, but that's not unusual. Help yourself by breaking your goals up into bite-size pieces. Some call it "eating an elephant one bite at a time." As ridiculous as that may sound, it is an interesting way to describe tackling your goals and making them short-term. It is easier to accomplish what you need to do using this technique.

Chapter 41

Take Care of YOU

Most of us are so busy with life that even when we find out we are sick, we barely have time to catch our breath before we are off and running and involved in a personal project, family responsibilities, work-related issues, etc. Oftentimes, the balance that is so necessary for good health either never was a part of our life or has always been elusive.

However, now you find out that you have a medical problem to deal with and wonder where you will find the time for doctor visits, lab tests, and possibly even time off for surgery or treatment. You are already stretched thin; you didn't need a health problem on top of everything else that's going on in your life.

Consider this:

Don't try to be all things to all people, especially during stressful times. Get enough rest and exercise (if you can exercise). Try to eat properly. Don't eat foods that are high in calories and fat. Let other people take on more responsibility including your children and other family members. Nothing is so important that it cannot wait, with the exception of your healing. Your number one priority is getting back to good health and that means taking care of YOU in every way that you know how.

Chapter 42

Create an Inner Peace Through Meditation

Many people meditate and find it extremely relaxing and helpful in relationship to medical problems. Unfortunately, Americans seem to be rather distrustful when it comes to meditation. Some people do not even want to close their eyes much less try to work the power of the mind over the body. Others see it as silly or strange.

Here is an interesting example of how meditation can work: At the Columbia Presbyterian Medical Center in New York City, heart patients are offered an optional program of massage, yoga and meditation. According to Dr. Mehmet Oz, Director of Columbia Presbyterian's Heart Institute, the researchers at the hospital have conducted randomized trials in which some patients get ninety minute tapes and others get sham mantras—meaningless scripts of random phrases. They discovered that the words did not matter. The patients who did the best in terms of managing pain and reducing anxiety were the ones who used the tapes, real or sham.

Consider this:

Whether you believe in the value of meditation or not, you may want to give it a try just to see what it is all about. You have nothing to lose and potentially something to gain. There is plenty of evidence that meditation can have a positive, long-term effect on chronic pain and mood. There is also documentation to support the use of meditation to control bleeding during surgery. At the very least, meditation may help you deal with your stress. Other benefits may be awaiting you in the medicine cabinet of your mind.

Chapter 43

Find One Good
Thing About Each Day

Each day that we have on this earth is special. Since my diagnosis and surgery I find that I look at every day differently from what I once did. Part of it is growing older, a privilege that I recognize. But part of it is remembering how I felt before and then immediately after the surgery. Prior to surgery I was on an emotional roller coaster and physically I was fighting to stay alive. I would not have lasted until the end of the year at the rate the tumor was growing. Unfortunately, I did not enjoy each day during the time of my illness. I made myself miserable fretting over something that I could not change or control.

When people are sick, it is easy to forget about the good that surrounds us in terms of family and friends, excellent medical professionals, and new technology for diagnosing and treating. If we were living one hundred years ago, medical outcomes would be very different from what they are today. How fortunate we are!

Consider this:

The human spirit is amazingly resilient. I know that if you work hard at maintaining a positive attitude you will find an inner strength that may surprise you. Illness can mentally immobilize us, but we are still in charge of our thoughts. Depression offers no benefits and the sooner you get over it, the better you will feel.

If you choose to seek professional help, I applaud you for that decision. Under certain circumstances trying to figure this all out alone can be nearly impossible. You need every ounce of your physical and emotional strength to fight your illness.

Make a commitment to yourself today to look for one good thing about each day no matter how bad things may look to you. Do not go to bed at night until you have identified that one good thing. Write it down, maybe in your journal. Chances are you will make this a habit, and that's even better.

Chapter 44

Avoid Negative People

Negative people have a tendency to pull us down. They may not even realize that they have the power to impact others as they do, but the fact is that they can be very destructive. On the other hand, for some it may be a game to see how many people they can take down with them. Unfortunately, most of us know people who fit into this category.

For example, Frank and his wife Susan were those kinds of people. I've known them both for years and I suspected their negative attitudes would definitely interfere with my recovery, and I was correct. They complain about everything; nothing is ever right or good enough. Their world looks depressing to them and they make sure that everyone knows how they feel.

I made a conscious effort to stay away from them. I knew for my own mental health that I didn't need friends like them, even though they may have meant well. It was the right decision; I have not seen them since before my surgery. I think they got the message. I healed both physically and mentally without their "help."

Consider this:

Avoid negative people, as they may hurt your chances for a speedy and complete recovery. Their poor attitudes may be unintentional, but can harm you at a time when you are especially vulnerable. I strongly recommend that you gradually move your relationship with negative people further and further away. Find reasons not to associate with them if you have to. They will eventually get the hint.

This may sound unfriendly or even appear to be a drastic measure when it comes to your relationship with friends and/or family members, but we are talking about your survival. Do what you have to do to make it work even if it means losing a friend or two. People that are potentially hurting your chances for a full recovery are the last thing you need right now. You need your energy to get back on your feet, not deal with the negative people in your life.

Chapter 45

Be Sensitive to Your Spiritual Consciousness

The relationship between healing and spiritual consciousness seems to be working. I have many friends for whom their faith has been their lifeline to eventual good health even though recovery didn't happen overnight. They insist that their religion and church or synagogue congregations were instrumental in their healing along with the power of prayer. Who are we to argue with that?

Consider this:

I guess that you could say that those who are healed and attribute their healing to their faith and religion would have healed on their own without spiritual help. Others may say that a leap of faith saw them through to a miracle. It does not matter what you believe, but if you do believe in a higher power, you may want to initiate a spiritual connection if you haven't already.

Here's a suggestion that you might find appealing. Get your name put on as many healing prayer lists as you can. Most churches have prayer lists and are open to including strangers as well as parishioners. There have actually been studies on the power of prayer lists in the healing process. I was fortunate to have had my name submitted (with my permission) to more than a dozen healing prayer lists throughout the country. Friends took the initiative and had me included on the lists in their churches. It was as simple as letting my friends know that I was open to the idea. I believe that all of those prayers helped in my recovery.

Chapter 46

Stay Active

If you are physically able to stay active while you are ill, it is one of the best gifts you can give yourself. Despite serious illness, you may have an opportunity to continue some of the social activities you enjoy. A natural reaction is to put on your blinders and block out the world. A more sensible approach is to stay active and involved.

For example, if you can exercise, even if you can just walk on a regular basis, it will give you strength and help you emotionally take a break from the physical as well as the emotional side of illness. Even a trip to the local cinema is a way to stay active as well as catch up on the newest movies. The word "active" means different things to different people, but I am sure you know what I mean.

Consider this:

Staying active when the doctor has bad news is about the last thing you want to do. However, activity can be one of the best therapies anyone could prescribe. Look for opportunities to do just that. Do not give up the things that you have always enjoyed doing unless you absolutely have to.

Activities might include a trip to the little theatre in your community, water aerobics, shopping for groceries, meeting friends for lunch or dinner, organizing a closet or attending a walk or run for charity. The list of ideas on ways to stay active and involved is limited only by your imagination. In most cases, it is more mental than physical. You just have to make up your mind that you are going to stay active and then get involved. Sitting around and feeling sorry for yourself will not improve your situation.

Chapter 47

Act Like a Person You Respect

Illness can do strange things to people including strip us of our self-esteem. If that happens, we lose respect for ourselves and that can be disastrous. My self-esteem has always been pretty good. However, illness threatened to rob me of every last bit that I had until I looked into the mirror and shouted, "Don't do this to yourself. You are stronger than that!" It was a start, but acting like a person I respect hasn't always come easily. It is very important if one is to fully recover emotionally. Logically I know this, but in reality, there were days when I still had to work at it, and you will too. Is it worth the effort? You bet!

Consider this:

Think of a role model, someone you respect and admire. How would that person act if he or she were in your situation? As an example, Christopher Reeve and Michael J. Fox are people who, despite their medical problems, are resilient and respectful of themselves. They set the example for anyone who has received bad news from the doctor. Their game plans were changed just like ours were changed yet they refuse to give up. Yes, they are celebrities, but they are also human beings, and they undoubtedly have experienced the same emotions that we have experienced.

Chapter 48

Don't Let Stress Get a Stranglehold

Stress is an inevitable part of life. In fact, without it a lot of things would never get accomplished. We rely upon stress to push us forward; a certain amount of stress is good. However, when the stress of family responsibilities, your job, and health problems hit you all at once, you may feel as if you are in a stranglehold. Uncontrolled stress can add to anxiety and make you feel even worse. Stomach distress, headaches, and heart palpitations can all result from stress. The best thing that you can do for yourself is learn how to manage it.

Consider this:

The next time you feel stressed, force your mind to think back to times when you felt in control and serene. Now visualize what it feels like to be "unstressed." Hold those thoughts. Practice this technique until it becomes second nature. As mentioned previously, exercise can be another great stress reliever and may even prevent too much stress from occurring in the first place.

You might also want to consider reading survival stories about people who have overcome their illnesses. They are living healthy and productive lives today despite accidents, disasters, or diagnoses with serious problems. Let them and their stories help you release your stress. Find these survivors through the Internet or your local library. Learn how they succeeded in conquering their stress and apply it to your own life.

There are lots of strategies for dealing with stress; for starters, many of them can be found in books on the subject of stress management. Try Internet sites such as the Mind/Body Medical Institute at www.mbmi.org that offers scientifically proven ways to reduce stress.

Chapter 49

Uplift Your Spirit With Positive Affirmations

A lot of simple, but profound affirmations, have been written and shared. Some are in the form of quotations while others are merely a few words recorded on slips of paper. Some of my favorite affirmations are quotations and include the following:

- One of the secrets of life is to make stepping stones out of stumbling blocks. –James Penn

- Never regret. If it's good, it's wonderful. If it's bad, it's experience. –Victoria Holt

- There is no such thing in anyone's life as an unimportant day. –Alexander Woollcott

- Change your thoughts and you change the world. –Harold R. Mcalindon, author

- Worry is a misuse of the imagination. –Dan Zadra

- If life doesn't offer a game worth playing, then invent a new one. –Anthony J. D'Angelo, author

- If the stable gate is closed, jump the fence. –Julie Krone, jockey

- Life is a great big canvas; throw all the paint on it you can. –Danny Kaye

- Some think it's holding on that makes one strong;
  sometimes it's letting go. –Sylvia Robinson

Consider this:

Look for "positivities" in the things that you enjoy
reading including books, newspapers and magazines. They
are all around us. Select the ones that have the most
meaning for you just as I did in the above-mentioned
examples. Carry them with you and read them when you
are stuck in traffic or simply need a mental lift.

Chapter 50

Practice Spontaneous
Acts of Kindness

Tim confided in Jeff that he needed someone to help his
wife find a support group for breast cancer survivors. Tim
did not know where to begin. His wife was depressed and
desperately in need of a connection with other women
going through what she was experiencing. Although Jeff's
wife did not have breast cancer, she volunteered to take
Tim's wife to a local support group meeting. That was all
Jeff's wife needed to get started in feeling comfortable with
a group of strangers who shared her pain.

In another example, a neighbor's dog jumped the fence
and escaped. An animal lover that happened to see the

dog coaxed it into her car. The friendly pup was wearing a collar with his identification. The rescuer phoned the frantic owner who picked him up eleven miles from home. Dozens of cars had passed the dog on the highway, but only one person stopped to help the lost retriever called "Wings."

Consider this:

Helping people is a wonderful way to speed your healing process. And when your efforts are spontaneous acts of kindness, others benefit too. Kindness could be in the form of a phone call to a lonely or elderly person or an offer to run an errand. Accompanying a frightened friend to his or her doctor's appointment would be greatly appreciated by someone who would never ask for your help. Kindness comes in many forms. Decide where you can make a difference.

Chapter 51

Create a "Jar of Joy"

Here is a wonderful idea that was shared with me by an old friend. He calls it a "Jar of Joy." I found it very helpful in my efforts to stay positive. Make a list of as many things as you can think of that make you laugh. Cut the list into strips and put them into a jar that is decoratively labeled "Jar of Joy." When you need an emotional boost, pull out a slip of paper and read the sentence out loud.

My "Jar of Joy" contains over 100 positive ideas that include things such as call my Uncle who is one of the funniest people I know. Another is to watch the swim class for 5-year-olds at the local YMCA—they are adorable and so determined. The third thing that never fails to make me laugh is watching the antics of a variety of birds at the feeders in my backyard.

Consider this:

All it takes is some creative thinking and a willingness to write down the ideas that come to mind. Try it and I can almost guarantee that your personal "Jar of Joy" will help keep you laughing. The more colorful the strips of paper, the better. Have fun decorating the jar or better yet, get your family or friends involved in helping you make your jar as enticing as possible. You want it to call out to you every day so that you find yourself looking forward to helping yourself to a joyful slip of paper!

Chapter 52

Don't Focus on the Negatives When You're Tired

When we are tired, it is hard to see the light at the end of the tunnel. It may seem easier to focus on the negatives.

There is something about being tired at the end of a day that does not mix well with positive thinking. During my illness, I found that I was at my lowest point of the day emotionally as evening approached. Everything looked bleak and I became more and more depressed as I thought about my circumstances and all of the things over which I had little or no control.

It finally occurred to me that the end of the day was not a good time to talk or think about things that were worrying me. I suddenly had a "light bulb" moment and realized that I had to tackle those kinds of issues first thing in the morning, a habit I have acquired and apply to this day.

Consider this:

Avoid thinking about depressing things when you are tired. It is not easy to do, but try to bottle your negative thoughts or mentally put them into a box and seal it for the night. Alternatively, substitute techniques or exercises that will take your mind off yourself and help you focus on the positives in your life. If you feel compelled to focus on the negatives, which is normal, wait until daylight when your outlook will most likely be better.

If you are still having problems with depression even during the day (which is not uncommon), you may want to seek professional counseling. I have mentioned this earlier in the book, but I believe that it bears repeating.

Chapter 53

Celebrate Milestones

Illness creates a difficult situation for most people. It is a time when we often forget to look at our accomplishments For example, chemotherapy was successful and radiation is not necessary. The cancer was caught in time and you do not need a mastectomy, but only a lumpectomy. You have had the surgery, and your arteries are pumping the blood you need to keep your heart beating and you living. Or you were one of the lucky ones to receive a transplant, and it is not rejecting. These are examples of milestones in the treatment process. Some may be small while others are significant, but they are all worth recognizing.

Consider this:

Celebrate your milestones! Celebrate mentally and then do something special to remind yourself of what you have achieved. Your celebration could be as simple as allowing yourself more time to enjoy a special interest. I celebrate by rewarding myself time on the Internet or giving myself time to write an article for a professional journal or write a chapter for a new book. I may also take time to read, call a friend to share my good news, or simply relax on the patio. The important thing is that you do *something* special to celebrate the milestones.

Chapter 54

Take a Deep Breath

Most people don't give any thought to where their next breath is coming from. Did you know that on average we take more than 20,000 breaths every 24 hours? Within one minute six liters of air moves in and out of our lungs. When we are under a lot of stress, it is not uncommon to get short of breath. There were instances during my illness when I was aware that my breathing was shallow. At other times, I had trouble catching my breath; I wondered if I would eventually run out of oxygen.

Although breathing comes naturally, stress can interfere with our breathing patterns. In addition, oxygen plays a vital role in our circulatory and respiratory systems. As we breathe, oxygen that is inhaled purifies our blood by removing poisonous waste products that are circulating throughout our blood systems. Our organs need oxygen to stay healthy so when we breathe too shallowly or quickly it impacts chest muscles, blood vessels, heart rates and more. Sometimes we may even unconsciously hold our breath.

Consider this:

Breathing and relaxation techniques are often taught in hospital and rehabilitation centers. All you have to do is inquire. Breathing exercises are especially helpful in treating anxiety, asthma, depression, heart disease, chronic

91

fatigue, high blood pressure, insomnia, menopause, PMS and plain old stress. Before beginning any breathing exercises it is essential that you learn how to breathe properly.

To start, lie down on a flat surface with your legs straight and slightly apart, your toes pointed comfortably outwards, arms at your sides not touching your body, your palms up, and your eyes closed. This is called a "relaxed body" position. Mentally visualize your body relaxing and breathe freely. Keep your mouth closed as you breathe.

Keep breathing and be aware that your chest and abdomen should move together. If only your chest seems to rise and fall, your breathing is too shallow and you are not making good use of the lower part of your lungs. As you inhale you should feel your abdomen rising; it is as if your stomach is filling with air.

As you exhale, your abdomen should come back in, like a balloon releasing all of its air. This inhale and exhale process should continue comfortably and smoothly. Your chest and abdomen should rise as you inhale and fall as you exhale. Your chest should move only slightly.

There is plenty of information on the subject of breathing techniques so I am not going into detail here. However, I do recommend one of Dr. Andrew Weil's books called, *Spontaneous Healing*. He recommends and describes five breathing exercises that I have tried and found very helpful. In fact, his entire book is a detailed resource of excellent health-related information. He also has a wonderful monthly on-line as well as hard-copy newsletter.

Chapter 55

Create Delightful Daily Habits

There are certain things most of us do every day like wash our hair in the morning, brush our teeth after meals, and go to bed when we are tired. Most of us have some type of routine when it comes to our daily habits, but routines can get boring.

Here is an example: Eric has HIV. He has certain procedures that he must follow every day to stay alive. Bill is on kidney dialysis and he too must follow a routine that is not always something he looks forward to. In each case, their regular habits are necessary, but both men sometimes get tired of doing what they have to do to continue to live.

Consider this:

Regardless of what your daily routine looks like, make a decision to create some new daily habits just for fun. For example, I mentioned laughter in a preceding chapter. Make looking for laughter and silly things a new and delightful daily habit. Be sure to make a mental or written note when you have found something that fits into this category. Consider doing something to pamper yourself every day as part of your daily habits. Maybe you will decide to take a bubble bath, or enjoy a glass of wine with a meal, or e-mail a special friend just to say "hello." All of these habits can be done on a daily basis to break up boredom. Whatever you decide to add to your list of daily habits, do not be afraid to get creative. Make a conscious effort to make the next habit one that's "delightful."

Chapter 56

Open Your Mind to Simple Pleasures

Part of the point of this chapter is the importance of stopping to smell the roses, but it goes beyond that. There are dozens of simple and oftentimes, unexpected pleasures for us to enjoy everyday. They surround us, but unless we are conscious of these wonderful things, we could easily miss them.

For example, I see a simple pleasure in a sip of water from a mountain spring or in admiring one white rose on my trellis of solid red roses. Every winter when I see the single white flower among the sea of crimson, I cannot help but be reminded of the saying that God gave us memory so that we might have roses in December. Simple pleasures—they are all around us.

Consider this:

Make a conscious effort to seek out the simplest of pleasures. It might be the scent of your favorite perfume, the hummingbird passing through your neighborhood on his way to a warmer climate for the winter or the sounds of nature at your campsite next to the lake late at night.

The pleasures in life appear in many forms and are sometimes even disguised. You may have to look hard to find them, but they really are on the surface in most cases. Just keep looking for the little things that can help to give you a mental boost. Don't miss the opportunity to enjoy what the world has to offer in the way of ordinary, but simple pleasures.

Chapter 57

Illness Can Reinvent Your Life

My philosophy has always been that something good comes from something bad. However, I had a tough time believing it when I was diagnosed. What could possibly be good about this medical nightmare? During my recovery, I kept looking for the good in the depression that I felt. Every time I looked at my paralyzed face, it made me sick.

However, my life was slowly reinventing itself, starting with many new tumor buddies whom I have met via the telephone and the Internet, as well as in person. I have lots of wonderful new friends, and we share many of the same feelings. I've found the connection to be invaluable. If I had not had the tumor, I would have never met these incredibly special people.

I have also developed a great relationship with my surgeons and have referred others to their gifted hands. The doctors who were involved in my case are awesome human beings. To this day, if I call or e-mail any one of them, they are there for me despite the fact that I was just one of hundreds of patients that they see every year.

Because I make my living as a speaker and writer, I thought that my career was over due to my face. I actually went back to work not looking that great. My first audience was a group of health care professionals. They interrupted the first five minutes of my presentation with three rounds of applause followed by a standing ovation at the end of the speech. Little did they know how they boosted my morale!

Today, among other types of organizations, I speak to health care professionals at association conferences as well as hospital meetings and conventions. My brain tumor experience has added lots of credibility to my motivational speeches, something that I would have preferred to have done without, but that's the way life goes.

Consider this:

Look for the good in the things that you cannot change. As mentioned earlier, try keeping a journal. Record your thoughts. Inventory your skills, interests, strengths and special gifts. These things are your lifelines to the future and a better tomorrow. Do not be afraid to reinvent your life. Use the ideas in this book to help you reach your destination.

Chapter 58

Let Go of the Game Plan

We all long for certain things in life, but sometimes our hopes and dreams slip away due to an unexpected illness. When that happens, it inevitably leads to letting go of the game plan. We have wanted something for so long and then everything suddenly changes. I could have never imagined that I would face, of all things, a brain tumor. That happens to other people, but not to someone like me who has always been health-conscious and fitness-oriented.

Sometimes I still wonder what happened and why it happened to me in the prime of my life. Why couldn't I have been diagnosed at age 85? I might not have had the surgery because of my advanced age. And if I had and my face was paralyzed, it probably would not have been as important to me as it is now. I will never know the answer as to why I was "chosen" for this particular journey, but thankfully, I have come to accept what has happened to me. I continue to volunteer my time to help others who are dealing with health problems, especially brain tumors.

Consider this:

Letting go of your game plan is about the uncontrollable and the fact that there are many things in life over which we have little or no influence. The reality can be heartbreaking, but moving on is essential if you are going to take advantage of what life has to offer beyond your present situation. There may come a time when you will need to let go of the game plan, develop a new one and embrace the future no matter what it holds for you.

Some Final Thoughts

I hope that by reading this book you have gained some insight into dealing with the anxiety associated with the bad news from your doctor. I have tried to openly share my thoughts, feelings and personal experience as much as I could. I encourage you to refer back to this book when you need help and use your time on earth to celebrate life every chance that you get. In addition, look for the positives and rejoice in all of the simple, but wonderful things that life has to offer. You have so much to live for!

I pray for your good health and wish you many years of happiness, enjoying life with those you love.

Carol A. Hacker

About the Author

Carol Hacker, president of Carol A. Hacker & Associates, is a business consultant, speaker, seminar leader, and author with over 25 years of management experience serving Fortune 100 as well as small businesses in the areas of change management, employee development, staffing and retention. The author of over 150 published articles and 11 business books, Carol is also a brain tumor survivor and strong advocate of being an informed patient. She earned her B.S. and M.S. with honors from the University of Wisconsin.

Appendix

The list of resources included in this Appendix has been verified and is up-to-date as of the printing of this book. Most of the phone numbers are toll free; a few are not. This list is not all-inclusive. However, I have tried to include as many organizations with their phone numbers and web sites as I could. They all offer free information, but a donation in exchange is always appreciated.

- **Acoustic Neuroma Association**
  1-770-205-8211 – www.anausa.org

- **ALS Association (Lou Gehrig's Disease)**
  1-800-782-4747 – www. alsa.org

- **Alzheimer's Association**
  1-800-272-3900 – www.alz.org

- **American Association of Kidney Patients**
  1-800-749-2257 – www.aakp.org

- **American Association on Mental Retardation**
  1-800-424-3688 – www.aamr.org

- **American Brain Tumor Association**
  1-800-886-2282 – abta.org

- **American Cancer Society**
  1-800-ACS-2345 – www.cancer.org

- **American Diabetes Association**
  1-800-342-2383 – www.diabetes.org

- **American Heart Association**
  1-800-242-8721 – www.americanheart.org

- **American Institute for Cancer Research**
  1-800-843-8114 – www.aicr.org

- **American Kidney Fund**
  1-800-638-8299 – www.kidneyfund.org

- **American Liver Foundation**
  1-800-465-4837 – www.liverfoundation.org

- **American Lung Association**
  1-800-586-4872 – www.lungusa.org

- **American Lupus Society**
  1-800-331-1802 – www.lupus.org

- **American Macular Degeneration Foundation**
  1-413-268-7660 – www.macular.org

- **American Parkinson's Disease Association**
  1-888-400-2732/1-800-223-2732
  www.apdaparkinson.org

- **American Psychiatric Association**
  1-888-357-7924 – www.psych.org

- **Aplastic Anemia & MDS International Foundation, Inc.**
  1-800-747-2820 – www.aamds.org

- **Arthritis Foundation**
  1-800-283-7800 – www.arthritis.org

- **Asthma and Allergy Foundation of America**
  1-800-7-ASTHMA – aafa.org

- **Autism Society of America**
  1-800-3AUTISM – www.autism-society.org

- **Brain Injury Association**
  1-703-761-0750 – www.biausa.org

- **Center for Disease Control National STDS and AIDS Hotline**
  1-800-227-8922/1-800-342-AIDS (2437)
  www.cdc.gov/ashastd.org

- **Children and Adults with Attention-Deficit/Hyperactivity Disorder**
  1-800-233-4050 – www.chadd.org

- **Crohn's and Colitis Foundation of America**
  1-800-932-2423 – www.ccfa.org

- **Cystic Fibrosis Foundation**
  1-800-344-4823 – www.cff.org

- **Depression and Bipolar Support Alliance (DBSA)**
  1-800-826-3632 – www.dpsalliance.org

- **Down's Syndrome Association**
  1-800-221-4602 – www.ndss.org

- **Endometriosis Association**
  1-414-355-2200 – www.endometriosisassn.org

- **Epilepsy Foundation**
  1-800-332-1000 – www.efa.org

- **Fibromyalgia Network**
  1-800-853-2929 – www.fmnetnews.com

- **First Candle/Sudden Infant Death Syndrome (SIDS) Alliance**
  1-800-221-7437 – www.firstcandle.com

- **Foundation Fighting Blindness**
  1-888-394-3937 – www.blindness.org

- **Gay Men's Health Crisis**
  1-800-243-7692 – www.gmhc.org

- **Genetic Alliance**
  1-800-336-4363 – www.geneticalliance.org

- **Glaucoma Research Foundation**
  1-800-826-6693 – www.glaucoma.org

- **Hydrocephalus Association**
  1-888-598-3789 – www.hydroassoc.org

- **Immune Deficiency Foundation**
  1-800-296-4433 – www.primaryimmune.org

- **International Cystitis Association**
  1-800-help.ica – www.ichelp.org

- **International Essential Tremor Foundation**
  1-888-387-3667 – www.essentialtremor.org

- **Intestinal Disease Foundation**
  1-877-587-9606 – www.intestinalfoundation.org

- **Juvenile Diabetes Foundation**
  1-800-533-CURE (2873) – jdf.org

- **Leukemia and Lymphoma Society**
  1-800-955-4572 – www.lls.org

- **Lupus Foundation of America**
  1-800-558-0121 – www.lupus.org

- **March of Dimes Birth Defects Foundation**
  1-888-663-4637 – www.marchofdimes.com

- **Muscular Dystrophy Association**
  1-800-572-1717 – www.mdausa.org

- Myasthenia Gravis Foundation of America
  1-800-541-5454 – www.myasthenia.org

- National Alliance for Research on Schizophrenia and Depression
  1-800-829-8289 – www.nasad.org

- National Alliance for the Mentally Ill
  1-800-950-6264 – www.nami.org

- National Alliance of Breast Cancer Organizations (NABCO) 1-888-80-NABCO – www.nabco.org

- National Alopecia Areata Foundation
  1-415-472-3780 – www.naaf.org

- National Association for the Visually Handicapped
  1-212-889-3141 – www.navh.org

- National Association of Anorexia Nervosa and Associated Disorders
  1-847-831-3438 – www.naad.org

- National Association of the Deaf
  1-301-587-1788 (voice) 1-301-587-1789 (TTY)
  www.nad.org

- National Attention Deficit Disorder Association
  1-847-432-ADDA – www.add.org

- National Breast Cancer Coalition
  1-800-622-2838 – www.stopbreastcancer.org

- National Burn Victim Foundation
  1-908-953-9091 – www.nbvf.org

- National Cancer Care Foundation, Inc./Cancer Care Inc.
  1-800–813-HOPE (4673) – www.cancercare.org

- **National Cancer Institute**
  1-800-4-CANCER – www.cancer.gov

- **National Childhood Cancer Foundation**
  1-800-458-6223 – www.nccf.org

- **National Children's Cancer Society**
  1-800-532-6459 – www.children-cancer.org

- **National Foundation for Depressive Illness**
  1-800-239-1265 – www.depression.org

- **National Hemophilia Foundation**
  1-800-424-2634 – www.hemophilia.org

- **National Institute of Neurological Disorders and Stroke**
  1-203-744-0100 – www.ninds.nih.gov/health

- **National Kidney Foundation**
  1-800-622-9010 – www.kidney.org

- **National Mental Health Association**
  1-800-969-NMHA – www.nmha.org

- **National Multiple Sclerosis Society**
  1-800-344-4867 – www.nmss.org

- **National Neurofibromatosis Foundation Inc.**
  1-800-323-7938 – www.nf.org

- **National Organization for Albinism and Hypopigmentation**
  1-800-473-2310 – www.albinism.org

- **National Organization for Rare Disorders**
  1-800-999-6673 – www.rarediseases.org

- **National Osteoporosis Foundation**
  1-800-231-4222 – www.nof.org

- **National Ovarian Cancer Coalition, Inc.**
  1-888-OVARIAN – www.ovarian.org

- **National Parkinson Foundation, Inc.**
  1-800-327-4545 – www.parkinson.org

- **National Prostate Cancer Coalition**
  1-888-245-9455 – www.pcacoalition.org

- **National Psoriasis Foundation**
  1-800-723-9166 – www.psoriasis.org

- **National Reye's Syndrome Foundation**
  1-800-233-7393 – www.reyessyndrome.org

- **National Rosacea Society**
  1-888-NO-BLUSH – www.rosacea.org

- **National Spinal Cord Injury Association**
  1-800-962-9629 – www.spinalcord.org

- **National Stroke Association**
  1-800-STROKES – www.stroke.org

- **National Women's Health Network**
  1-202-628-7814 – www.womenshealthnetwork.org

- **Ovarian Cancer National Alliance**
  1-202-331-1332 – www.ovariancancer.org

- **Paget Foundation**
  1-800-23PAGET(72438) – www.paget.org

- **Scleroderma Foundation**
  1-800-722-HOPE – www.scleroderma.org

- **Scoliosis Association**
  1-800-800-0669 – www.scoliosis-assoc.org

- Sickle Cell Disease Association of America, Inc. (SCDAA)
  1-800-421-8453 – www.sicklecelldisease.org

- Sjögren's Syndrome Foundation
  1-800-475-6473 – www.sjogrens.com

- Skin Cancer Foundation
  1-800-SKIN-490 – www.skincancer.org

- Spina Bifida Association of America
  1-800-621-3141 – www.sbaa.org

- Thyroid Foundation of America
  1-800-832-832 – www.tsh.org

- Trigeminal Neuralgia Association
  1-904-799-0333 – www.tna-support.org

- United Cerebral Palsy Association
  1-800-872-5827 – www.ucpa.org

- United Ostomy Association
  1-800-826-0826 – www.uoa.org

- Vestibular Disorders Association (VEDA)
  1-800-837-8428 – www.vistibular.org

- Wilson's Disease Foundation
  1-800-399-0266 – www.wilsonsdisease.org

- Y-ME National Breast Cancer Organization
  1-800-221-2141 – www.y-me.org

Books and CDs by Carol

450 Low-Cost/No-Cost Strategies for recognizing, rewarding & retaining good people Volume II

366 MORE Surefire Ways to Let Your Employees Know They Count

How to Compete in the War for Talent—A Guide to Hiring the Best

Retain or Retrain: How to Keep the Good Ones from Leaving

366 Surefire Ways to Let Your Employees Know They Count

450 Low-Cost/No-Cost Strategies for recognizing, rewarding & retaining good people Volume I

Job Hunting in the 21st Century—Exploding the Myths, Exploring the Realities

The Costs of Bad Hiring Decisions & How to Avoid Them—1st and 2nd Editions

The High Cost of Low Morale ...and what to do about it

Hiring Top Performers—350 Great Interview Questions For People Who Need People

20 Costly Hiring Mistakes and How to Avoid Them – 47 minute CD

How to Conduct "Win-Win" Performance Evaluations – 75 minute CD

Low-Cost-No-Cost Strategies for Motivating Your Employees – 69 minute CD

An Invitation From the Author

Carol encourages you to contact her with comments, questions, and things that you do to keep a positive attitude during illness. This book will be updated periodically and if your idea is included in the next printing, you will receive a free copy of the book.

She welcomes opportunities to speak at association conferences, conventions, planning retreats, and other organizational and corporate functions. Additionally, she is available to conduct workshops and provide consulting services.

Carol can be reached at:

Carol A. Hacker & Associates
209 Cutty Sark Way
Alpharetta, Georgia 30005
Phone - 770-410-0517
Fax - 770-667-9801
www.carolahacker.com
carol@carolahacker.com

Index

A

B

Bible 68
big picture 71, 72
biopsy 71
bite-size pieces 73
blame 20, 21
blessings 20, 25, 37
blood type 59
body language 4
Bombeck, Erma 38
brain tumor vi, xi, 7, 36, 71, 96, 100, 101
Brininstool, Christine x
broken toe 71
bubble bath 68, 93

C

calories 32, 74
campsite 95
cancer 6, 16, 17, 20, 27, 39, 42, 44, 51, 70, 86, 90, 101, 104, 105, 106
Cancer Hope Network 17
candlelight dinner 26
captain 8, 9, 10
carbohydrates 33
card game 22
caregiver 26, 49, 60, 63
carpool 7
CT scans 5
cataract surgery 45
CD 58, 108
celebrate 73, 90, 99
celebrated vii
centerwatch.com 17
central record keepers 57

D

F

facial 69
  facial re-animation therapy 72
faith 40, 79, 80
fat 33, 74
  fats 33
fear vi, 14, 29, 39
  fearful 39
  fearing the worse 9
feeling guilty 7
feelings of anxiousness 11
Ferris, Rosemary x
fiber 33
Foreward v
forward-thinking attitude 2, 23, 24
Fox, Michael, J 83
Franklin, Benjamin 70
Friedman, Rick A., M.D., PhD. vii
Friends Health Connection 17
fruits 33
Funicello, Annette 1

G

"good news" inventory 2, 36, 37
gallbladder removal 45
game show 38
genetic disease 20
goal 14, 48, 73
goals 72, 73
Gonzales, Brigette vii
Graham, Reverend Billy 65
grandchildren 69

gratitude 26, 61, 62, 69
grief viii
grieve viii, 19
grieve the loss viii, 72
grieved xii
grieving process viii, 18
guilt 21
guilty 7

H

haircut 32
handwritten note 46
healing prayer lists 80
healing process 3, 80, 87
health care team 8, 9, 10
healthfinder.gov 16
healthy eating 32, 33
herbal supplement 52
herbal treatments 35
herbs 34, 35
high blood pressure 92
higher power 80
Hitselberger, William, M.D. vii
HIV 93
holistic 34, 35
holistic approach 34, 36
    holistic medicine 35
Holt, Victoria 85
hospital x, 10, 39, 47, 56, 57, 60, 62, 63, 64, 73, 75, 92, 96
    appointments 7
    bed 18
    food 62
    staff 72

M

motivational tool 2
multiple sclerosis 6, 105

N

National Women's Health Resource Center 16
National Institute of Health 16, 17
negative people 78, 79
Newcorn, Rene x
new technology 77
non-verbal communication 26
nutrients 32

O

obstacles 2
open-minded doctors 6
opinions 44, 45, 52
options 3, 35, 43, 45, 46, 47, 55
oxygen 20, 91
Oz, Mehmet, Dr. 75

P

"pity party" 18, 19
"positivities" 86
paralyzed 5, 9, 14, 72, 95, 87
Parkinson's disease 6
Parkinson's Disease Association 102
passionate 66
Penn, James 85
Pharmacist 61
physical challenge 13
poetry 69
positive attitude 4, 19, 77, 109

positive self-talk 4, 24
potential problems 64
power of prayer 80
power of prayer lists 80
pneumonia 53
Precious Present, The 40
Preas, Stephen, M.D. vii
Preface viii
primary care physician 55
professional counseling 5, 90
protein 32, 33
psychiatrist x, 11
psychological stress 6
psychologist 11

Q

quackwatch.org 35

R

"release of medical information" form 58
radiation x, 36, 39, 90
reading lips 41
reality vi, 6, 4, 5, 22, 28, 39, 82, 98
reciprocity 8
recovery 3, 4, 5, 10, 17, 19, 24, 72, 73, 78, 79, 80, 96
recovery phase of your illness 17
Reeve, Christopher 83
reflexology 34
rehabilitation program 72
reinvent your life 95, 97
relaxation techniques 92
religion 80
religious organization 14

T

W

"wacky" approaches to healing 35
walking 23, 31
warning signs 30
water 30, 95
  aerobics 82
Web MD 17
web sites 3, 16, 17, 101
Weil, Andrew, M.D. 35, 93
Williams, Jeffery, M.D. vii
Woollcott, Alexander 85
World Health Organization 17
World Trade Center bombings 24

X

x-rays 37, 58

Y

YMCA 73, 88
Yoga 75

Z

Zadra, Dan 85

Notes